BLACK BUTTERFLY

**Short Films
by Darren S. Hardaway Jr.**

*Hardcase
Chat!
Psalm 23*

Ladyofchoice.com

BLACK BUTTERFLY

Rebirth of a Beautiful Soul

DARREN S. HARDAWAY JR.

This is a work of fiction. Names, characters, businesses, places, and events are either the products of the author's imagination or are used in a fictitious manner. Any resemblance to actual persons, living or dead, or actual events is purely coincidental.

ISBN: 978-1-7361063-0-3 - Paperback
eISBN: 978-1-7361063-1-0 - ePub
eISBN: 978-1-7361063-2-7 - mobi

Library of Congress Control Number: 2021903185

Printed in the United States of America   0 3 0 8 2 1

♾This paper meets the requirements of ANSI/NISO Z39.48-1992 (Permanence of Paper)

Cover Art: Adrianna Wilder, MUSA Brand www.gomusa.com

Photographer: Jan Decino, Jay Capture Media

Logo Design: Caitlin Campbell, Soup Graphic Design, www.SoupGraphicDesign.com

Scripture quotations are taken from the Holy Bible, King James Version (Public Domain).

This book is dedicated to my grandma, great-grandma, and Aunt Jean, and to all the actual names that have been mentioned in this book, you know who you are. All of you have been a part of my journey. I am thankful that I was able to witness the experiences that we have shared together. I thank you and I love you all!

To give light to those who sit in darkness and in the shadow of death guide our feet into the way of peace. I dedicate that prayer to the brothers and sisters who are ill, sick, poor, homeless, and incarcerated. May you all have the strength, the will, and the health to get through whatever you may be going through. Peace and Love be upon you all! Amen.

And finally:

To the DREAMERS and BELIEVERS, MAKE IT HAPPEN!

I can do all things through Christ which strengtheneth me.
                    —Philippians 4:13

Hate is never greater than Love.

Disclaimer: This is a fictional story inspired by true events.

The following material is intended for mature audiences and contains explicit sexual situations, depictions of violence or abuse, and other adult content. Reader discretion is advised.

This story of mine is not to reminisce on my past doings, or dwell on the carnage I left behind. But, I tell this story because I am the author of my story! I am the motivator behind all my actions, with applied faith. My past is what allowed me to live in the moment, to be present. I am the definer of who I am, no man or woman can rob me of my jewels. My brothers and my sisters, the kings and queens, we may not have traveled the same road, committed the same actions, but every tear we ever shed came from pain, all the blood that was ever spilled came from hurt. Even though we can't undo what we did, what we can do is to do better than what we did. Make use of every tool we were blessed with, from the lessons we endured during our struggle—the fire came ashes, our storm—the rain—came sun. The travels in my life are what allowed me to strap up and put boots on the ground. To be able to extend my cable-tow as far as I can to be that helping hand, the vessel that aids the next brother or sister in their own pursuit of purpose. I tell my life's journey not just for me, but for the ones who feel helpless, abandoned, stuck in a place where you feel you can't get out. Just know, I've been there. I encourage you to walk your own path, live in your own truth. Tell your story because YOU matter. Love yourself, believe in yourself, and believe in what you believe in, even if no one else does. I love you.

FAITH, FOCUS, FORWARD. This is my testimony!

He is I and I am him.

Alexander Lee Jr.

CONTENTS

CHAPTER ONE

Dissimilar Norms

Our perception in life is tailored by the things that our senses become exposed to. I grew up with the impression that wrong was right. That is what my mother ingrained in me. Acts of cruelty, love is pain—that is what was normal to me.

Born in 1982 on 7642 South Perry Street on the South Side of Chicago, Illinois, I was hell bound before I was born. I spent only a few years with my parents. More time with my mother than I had with my father. This was because my parents were both murdered by a gunshot wound to the head. Father when I was at the age of six and Mother at the age of nine. Preceding my father's death, I did not know the variant lifestyle he lived outside the home. Times we did share, he would always allude to be better than him. At that age, I could not see what he was trying to say.

The difference between him and my mom is that my father was never violent with me. I was his balance in between his two worlds. Every time my father would leave to go out of town, it would allow my mother to discipline me the way that she wanted. Physical abuse, mental abuse, it did not matter. She would use her hands, belts, cords, her words, take a hot shower but do not dry off, it would leave the body tender for whatever she would be in the mood for. At the end of those beatings, she would comfort me with hugs and kisses, telling me that she loved me. So, that is where I formed the notion love is pain.

I was six years old, riding my bike my father bought me around the block. Nobody in the area would hassle me because I was Alexander Lee Sr.'s son. The son of an outlaw. Murderer for hire, him and my Uncle Earl. My father lost his way, from the brutality of slaughtering a family of three, with the third being just an infant. He was dedicated to the oath he took. His objective was to kill them all. That was the assignment he carried out for "The Devil's Kings" a week before his death.

My father tried to mask his suffering with heavy drug use. Each prick of the needle caused his behavior to only get worse. Not violent, but more distant. Not just with me and Mom, but himself. A man who was once so strong that the ground he walked on would tremble. But after the death of the newborn, my daddy could barely stand on his own two feet.

But on that day, it was hot out, summertime in Chicago. Normally, the neighbors would be outside, watering their garden, mowing the lawn, sitting on their porch chitchatting about the other folks on the block, discussing who was up to no good. This day was different. Silent. It was like you could feel that the devil was approaching. I walked my bike up to the vestibule of our home and noticed my mother sitting down, inhaling a cigarette, a box of Salem Lights 100 resting on her lap. Only time I ever saw my mother smoke was when she was done beating me. Thought that was how she regained her energy. But she had not put her hands on me, nor had she said anything foul to me. So, I was unclear of what was going on.

I placed my bike down and walked over to my mother and simply asked, "What's wrong?"

She replied, "Go play."

I did not know what to say. So, I asked, "Where's Dad?"

Nothing from my mom. She was tight-lipped. She looked in my direction, we became locked in, I was afraid. Mother seemed troubled, unemotional, as her eyes became watery. She rose from her seat, and without taking her eyes off me, she voiced, "I don't love your father anymore," and kissed me on the forehead as she moved her way toward the entrance of our home. As the front door slammed, thunder erupted, rain began to pour, the clouds assembled, the heavens darkened. I gazed into the sunless sky as the background noise of the television in our living room became louder. I went inside and moved around as I walked to the entrance of my parents' room.

My mother did not take into consideration that I was standing there, but my father did. The pain in his eyes, the tears he shed, a man who wanted to be saved but he knew he couldn't. A man who was fearless, but in that moment, he was scared. His lips moved to the struggle of his last breath that he spoke to me: "Show yourself a man." Never once did he stop looking at me as I looked at him. My mother was hovering over him, pointing the barrel of the rifle to his temple. That is when my mother finally acknowledged me standing in the doorway of their room.

Father was lying on the floor, covered in his own vomit. The last stand of Alexander Lee Sr. had come. Mom stretched over to grab a pillow off the bed, placing it on top of my father's head. Using her foot to hold it in place, she then pressed down on the pillow with the barrel of the rifle. Right before pulling the trigger, the echo of my mother's voice in my head saying she did not love my father any longer was all I heard. And then *boom*. The trigger was pulled.

Knowing the act was done, Mom seemed fine, relaxed, calm. Granted, it took her a second to collect her composure, but she was good. The lifeless body of my father lay at her feet. Raising her leg over the body, she came my way. Before passing me, she spoke softly, saying, "It's for his own good," as she exited the room. In a gingerly motion, I walked toward my father. A war raged within my own mind to suppress the last image of my father, which was forever rooted in my head. My father lay in a pool of his own blood, the fragments of his skull—chunks of his mind—scattered throughout the room. My parents' room was well-furnished, but it felt so empty. It was all there but I did not see it. The TV, the bookshelf, the bed, the dresser, the photos, and the chair. All I saw was the body of my father, stretched across the floor.

I swayed back and forth unsure of what to do. Should I leave it as is or do I remove the pillow off my father's head? I felt my mother's spirit enter the room. A chilly air ran across the back of my neck as she stood there in the doorway. But the wraith of my father still breathed life in the room. As I removed the pillow, little to none were the remains of my father's head. In amazement, I stepped back and stumbled over my father's corpse. I found myself on the ground, hands baptized in a pool of my father's sins. Tears came trickling down my face as my mother watched from afar. Without a word, she walked away.

Allowing time to go by, hours had passed, but with every second, the room became louder as I sat. Soon, night was upon us. The temperature of the room, which came from heat outside, created a rotten, seafood-like odor from the flesh and blood of my father's remains. I started hearing voices that were not mine. The voices became louder as my mother ushered two men into the room to view my father's body. They happened to be the same men who had come to clean up my father's body. Talking to me, my mother implied that I go shower, clean myself up. I was covered in blood. The first time she spoke to me, I did not hear her. I sat there in a trance, so she repeated herself.

"Alexander, you hear me? Go shower!" she said determinedly.

The death of my father weighed heavy on me. Tears fell down my face as the blood dripped off the palms of my hands and I realized this would be the last time I'd see my father outside of my own head.

Time persisted, life moved on, too heavy for a heart like mine. I wanted to be saved, but no one came. Not my father nor my uncle, and that's when Death was introduced to me. The idea of Death being a thief, taking you away from the life you lived, the family you loved, where all that is left of you is the memories you imposed on the people you have met and what you have done while on earth. Death is the biggest thief of them all because there is no escaping it.

But for my Uncle Earl, I thought he abandoned me. That was far from the truth. Mom was the answer to why Uncle Earl neglected me. She hated him, seeing as my Uncle Earl annihilated her only sibling, my mother's big brother. The narrative of how and why he did what he did—well, to the average mind it would be disturbing, gruesome at best. The news reporter said it was something that came from the word "macabre." Just because how he did it was so unearthly, but he did do it.

CHAPTER TWO

Family's Narrative

Alexander Lee Sr., an African American man born and raised in the inner city of Chicago, in a community called "Little Hell"—Lucifer's recreational ground. That is what my uncle called it, but it was the projects. Alexander Lee Sr. and his twin brother, Earl Lee, were known as "the Twins." Their name had a bigger effect on the community than the urban legend Candyman, who hunted and killed through the Chicago projects. In the film, men and women would lock themselves in a bathroom and turn off the lights. Saying his name, Candyman, five times in the mirror, he would emerge from the background. Standing behind you with a hook that was attached to the bloody stump of his right arm. Once he opened his mouth, bees would attack you. Without even knowing, being in so much fear, you wouldn't feel the hook go across your throat or cut through your stomach. That was the urban legend.

Their father was a pastor who preached the gospel. But when he was not standing behind the pulpit, he was a known gun trafficker. He would purchase weapons in Minnesota at a lower rate and come back to Chicago to resell for a profit to various organizations, such as gangs. He had a crew and they had a system. They would obtain the weapons through straw purchasers, who purchased weapons on their behalf because they were legally unable to do it themselves. They would also commit home invasions and store robberies to produce the quantity that they did. Semi-automatics, revolvers, rifles, shotguns, and stun guns, they became the neighborhood's number-one supplier and one of the ATF's top ten most wanted. But it all came to an end when employees were killed during an armed robbery at a gun shop in Minneapolis. His co-defendants were convicted of first-degree murder and ninety guns were stolen from that store that evening.

Their father knew his world was closing in on him, so he wanted to spend as much time with his kids as he could. One day, their father drove to a pay phone, leaving the Twins in the car. The same car that he would take the Twins out to let them drive. He would allow them to sit on his lap so they could turn the steering wheel while he accelerated. That was a way he would spend time with his kids, by teaching them how to drive. While on the pay phone, their father spotted a marked car parked not too far from where he had parked. He knew he was being followed. The call on the pay phone was to their mother, telling her to come pick them up as soon as possible. Their father drove to a nearby supermarket and waited until their mother arrived. Once she did, he said his goodbyes, giving hugs and kisses because he was not sure if his kids would ever be a part of his life again. Hugging his children, he was startled by the roaring sounds of police sirens. They became piercing to his ears. The sirens grew louder and louder as they got closer. He finally strapped the Twins in the back seat so they and their mother could leave. As she started to drive off, police units sped past her. Units came from every direction, cars pulling to the side, pedestrians running to get out of the way. The Twins were forced to witness as their father was handcuffed and accompanied to the back seat of a police patrol car.

Their father was held at the Stateville Maximum Correctional Facility for the duration of his sentence. His sons were only nine and now fatherless. My uncle said he would have looked at his father with love and respect if he had shot it out with the police, instead of allowing them to cuff him. Their dad was as good as dead in the eyes of my uncle. He allowed the system to enslave him, take him away from his family. See, if he died by gun, that concept would have been a lot easier to accept, but every day, a father—a man—is to be a protector, provider, promotor, a priest over his home, and a prophet to his family. Their sperm donor failed at his obligation of being a father. So, the responsibilities fell onto the hands of the mother to raise two boys.

As a single mother raising two boys in the projects on one source of income, my grandma was forced to work double jobs, pick up extra shifts, and do all she could to make sure her boys did not miss a meal. She spent more time at work than she did at home, so what can you expect? The Twins began to venture off into new beginnings.

The Twins went out looking for love, comfort, some family structure, and as they did, the Chicago streets embraced them with open arms. Lil Stace knew their father and he stepped up to fill that fatherly role. Lil Stace eventually became their guardian. A much older fellow who was president of a local motorcycle charter called "The Devil's Kings," Lil Stace helped develop the Twins' reputation throughout the city. He showed them how to lay down the law, build their reputation by being ruthless.

Lil Stace groomed my father and uncle from boys to men until their dying days. He molded two lost boys into full-blown murderers, educating the Twins with customary tools to survive in their world. Having the fundamentals to get by in your own world, learning what you must know, is truly all that matters. Understanding that the true meaning of being free is by using what you know to make your own decisions. The more you know, the more choices you have. Lil Stace taught them the properties of playing with fire, taught them the rules of engagement, taught them how to control and master their emotions and learn how to study an individual—watch what they build, watch what they say, watch what they do. I once heard a quote by John Steinbeck, "No man really knows about other human beings. The best he can do is suppose that they are like himself." Perhaps having a realization toward that concept is why taking a life became easy. That was what they identified in their surroundings, ignorant to gender bias—all genders, all races, all ages, capable of the unthinkable.

The wreckage that was caused by the hands of my family did not begin until that same year their father went to prison. Their mother, Monie, was visiting a friend of hers that evening, on the South Side of Chicago. As she was leaving her friend's apartment, a disrespectful little boy named Cain became verbally hostile toward Monie.

Cain's big homies who were around him should have put him in line for that disrespect. He showed lack of respect for himself and the ones he represented, ones who had raised him.

Days before that incident, my father had fought Cain. They had a fist fight, but my daddy and my uncle were sluggers; they knew how to fight. Within the community, standing in the scratch line was how you earned your respect by the fellow man and woman. It was something that started in the military. It allowed you to be physically capable of defending yourself at any given moment. Iron sharpens iron; you stand in line to fight until you can't fight no more. Back then, if you lost a fight, your family or friends would tell you to go fight again until you win or just go in the woods and prepare for disciplinary action. The ones you are with will jump you for sixty seconds. No face shots, only body. Train you to be tough, not afraid to be hit. That was the way they were brought up. So, Cain lost to my father. He saw an opportunity that presented itself and he took advantage of it. He had no parental guidance in his home. Father locked up, mother a junkie, he learned what he learned by being around his peers. That same night, the son of Monie's friend somehow got word to my father that Monie was being disrespected by Cain. He should have known better, but the greatest lessons in life are through life experience, so it's wise to be well-mannered and foolish to be rude.

The next day, my father and Uncle Earl went to Lil Stace for advice on how to go about managing this the proper way. The Twins had gathered as much information as they could to provide to Lil Stace on the whereabouts of

Cain. The school he attended. The project building he stayed in. First and last name.

Lil Stace was powerful everywhere he went. He was connected, respected, and he had rank amongst men. That morning, Lil Stace went over to the South Side and began his manhunt. A man of patience, he spent hours searching for Cain. Cain was at the candy store, right off the Dan Ryan. Lil Stace stalked him for a moment as Cain began to walk out of the store. Cain went down the alleyway because he figured it would be a short route to where he was headed. However, Lil Stace drove down the alley. As he came closer to Cain, he opened the driver-side door of his car, knocking Cain down. Cain's body became disabled from the impact of the car door. Lil Stace hopped out and tied Cain's wrists to his ankles and patched his mouth with duct tape. Now it was time for the Twins to earn their keep.

Lil Stace went to the projects to pick the Twins up and took them for a ride over to the South Side. By the time they pulled up to the projects, my father and uncle were still unaware of the live body in the truck. Lil Stace ordered everyone to exit his car. The Twins never questioned why they were at the projects but felt it had something to do with them and Cain. My uncle said when they pulled up and got out, you could feel a cold presence in the air, like death was looming around. This was the Twins' beginning of who they became.

Lil Stace proceeded toward the rear of his car as the Twins followed. Lil Stace's first words were, "Handle ya shit." As he opened the trunk, there he was: Cain. Eyes wide, hands and feet bound, mouth duct-taped, residue of tears on his face. The Twins had never once seen anything like it. This kid was scared. He was only fifteen years old and was not mentally prepared to be in a situation like this. You must be conditioned to withstand an activity as such, and when you do, you become militant. Systemically trained to endure the most. There is disassociation from the mind and the body to where you feel nothing. It is like a nerve blocker. A pigeonhole. Having a steady hand over a lighter, the flame would burn the flesh. You can smell the skin burning, blisters begin to form. But your mind goes into a trance where everything becomes numb. Compartmentalizing sensation and reality suppresses your thoughts and emotions. It's there, it is happening, but you don't feel it.

Residents were present at the time. It was morning and everyone was out, but that did not mean much. Lil Stace grabbed Cain out of the trunk and he rolled onto the ground. Lil Stace advised the Twins to get to it, which they did. Punching, kicking, jumping on him, they did that. Cain's mom was nearby and she caught a glimpse of her baby boy getting stomped out. Junkie or not, that was her kid. However, what she saw made her go into a full rage, and she grabbed a bat and made her way over. Before she got close, Lil Stace felt threatened by her having a bat, knowing she was an addict and most likely under the influence of drugs at that moment. Her actions would then be uncontrollable, so there was no telling what she would have tried. Inching closer, Lil Stace drew his .357 long-nose revolver and filled her body with two slugs. That was the first time the Twins witnessed Lil Stace murder someone, especially a woman. User or not, she was still a human. The death of the mother was a power play by Lil Stace, which was well played. He used that opportunity to his advantage to gain the Twins' loyalty.

Lil Stace then became agitated, telling the Twins that they needed to finish the job. Cain was bound and beaten. After the kicks, the punching, the stomping, the jumping, his body should have been numb to the pain. My father and uncle gathered what was left of Cain, still alive, but he was no longer present. Each on one arm, they dragged Cain's body into the complex, hauling the body up flights of stairs until they reached the rooftop. The Twins looked down as the neighbors looked up—men, women, and children. My father and uncle held Cain upside down by his ankles as his body dangled in the air. This was exciting to Lil Stace. As Lil Stace yelled, "Do it," the Twins let loose of his ankles, dropping Cain headfirst onto the steps of the complex.

The Twins walked out unbothered and sightseers watched as the Twins joined Lil Stace at his car and drove off. Lil Stace was not worried about telltales. Every project was administered by the local organizations. You didn't see nothing, you didn't hear nothing, you know nothing. That was a regulation for it to become a safeguard for your well-being and your family.

Later that night, their mother was already aware of her kids' sadistic behavior. She was told of the tragedy that had taken place at the projects. Her friend was the one who made the call to her. When the Twins finally arrived home, they were addressed by their mother. She had had time to prepare herself for this moment, time to think it through, cry as much as needed. She gave them an ultimatum. It was her or Lil Stace. Their mother was not there to breed killers. She wanted more for them, something better, that was why she worked so hard to provide, but it was just not enough. The more she worked, the more space it would create between her and her sons. Her fear after working a long shift was to receive a call from the Cook County coroner asking her to come view the body of one of her sons, as the other one was sent away to some correctional intuition next to their father. Just something a mother would not want to accept. To save her the headache, my father and uncle moved on. As they grew older, they knew that was the best choice to make. In all, it was for their mom's own sake. They knew by doing so, communication between their mother and her sons would end. They accepted everything that came with the decision they made. That night, everybody moved on.

Years later, Grandma moved to the suburbs, had two kids. A boy named Stacee and a daughter named Shavon. As her kids became adults, Shavon was pursuing a career in health care while raising a beautiful daughter and Stacee was finding his own way in life. That is all I really know about that family. My uncle learned this by doing research, just to make sure his mother was doing all right. Knowing that she was gave him joy.

The Twins grew older under the supervision of Lil Stace. He made honest men out of them, regardless of the criminal path they chose. One of the lessons Lil Stace told him, and that my uncle told me, is he made sure they understood that the judgement of others should not affect how you conduct yourself. Regardless of what someone thinks of you or what you have done, if you feel deep down that it was for the right reason, who cares what someone thinks of you? Just make sure you accept everything you do. Take responsibility for your own actions and move on. When you do, life becomes simple.

July 4, 1980. At the time, my daddy and uncle were sixteen years old. Lil Stace still sat at the head of the table for The Devil's Kings, and he allowed my father and uncle to partake in club activities. He never once allowed them to use or sell drugs, told them not to drink, and not to get involved with sex workers to earn a profit. Lil Stace was devoted to his idea of death-dealers, using the Twins to kill for the cause, nothing more, nothing less. He expressed to them that drinking put you in danger if you did not have control over yourself, because your mind was now altered; it left you exposed. Selling drugs or having sex workers work for you put you in a bind to where your sellers or users could give off credible intel about you to the local authorities or to the neighborhood jack boy looking for a score for that night. He wanted to shelter the Twins from unwarranted threats. Taught them that whatever you do, you do alone, or you build a crew of crooks ready and willing to die and destroy to defend you. Your crew does not eat, sleep, shit, or have sex until the job is done. That is how you structure your squadron. That is how the Twins formed the Legion of Doom. A death squad, the name originated from the WWE tag team The Road Warriors, Hawk and Animal. This group was freelance killers; some of them came from the military and that is how my father and uncle learned some new tactics and mental preparation. These men were prepared to kill and die on the orders they were told. That is how they were trained in the service. That now worked under The Devil's Kings.

On July 4, The Devil's Kings put together a family function: a BBQ for its members and their family. Food, drinks, fireworks, entertainers, jumpy house—they went above and beyond for every occasion they had. It was set for everyone to have an enjoyable time and feel safe. All the members of The Devil's Kings knew of the Twins and how valuable they were to Lil Stace. But the prospect, who was a regular guy, was trying to earn his way into the club. The prospect came to the gathering with his two older male cousins and his fourteen-year-old sister. At some point, the prospect walked away with the cousins, leaving his sister alone, where she knew no one. It was not safe for her to be left alone. The Devil's Kings are a one percent organization that condone in violence, such as drugs, murder, extortion, trafficking, etc. They formed their charter off the strength of crime. Drug dealers, pimps, murderers collectively came together for this event.

My father made sure no harm came her way. During this function, Lil Stace was teaching my uncle how to grill shrimp. While the prospect and the cousins went to smoke dope, my father walked off with the young lady to the portable toilet. My father was sixteen years old to her fourteen. After spending some alone time together, coincidentally, they all bumped into each other: the prospect, the cousins, my father, and her. Somewhere between talking, my father swung on the prospect and it connected, but the odds were stacked against him, three against one. Within that brief time, they got the best of him. Three grown men jumping on a sixteen-year-old kid, that's savagery.

By the time it was all broken up, my father lay there motionless, not dead, just unconscious. When my uncle found his brother, it was inadmissible; someone had to feel his pain. He had never seen his brother in the way he was in. Dead-like. My uncle was hurt that he had not been there for his brother. Under different circumstances, the prospect and the two cousins would have died where they stood, but out of the respect for brothers of the charter, my uncle did not react. He wanted this to be felt across the nation. Every action he took had its purpose. Play a sucker to catch a sucker.

Out of respect, Lil Stace did not interfere with my uncle's ambitions. Over the course of several weeks, my uncle was nonchalant in the presence of the prospect. He wanted the prospect to be at ease. He knew eventually the prospect would drop his guard, but if he were to attack sooner rather than later, the prospect would have been on edge, paranoid. He allowed time to go by; what you do not see you cannot fight. During that time, my uncle did his homework, became a master of disguise. He learned where the family of the prospect lived, which was in Joliet, home of his parents and siblings, his sister who religiously practiced in black magic, his own home over by Washington Park, which was highly publicized for its events, such as the Soul Circus. He had one child who attended CICS Washington Park, which was a grammar school. Those were the basics. My uncle further explained many nights he would sit outside the home of the prospect. He knew the times when the prospect would go out through the front door or back door of his home. The cousins were not persons of interest. As Matthew 26:31 tells, "I will smite the shepherd, and the sheep of the flock shall be scattered abroad." The cousins were not a threat. The remainder of their lives would be in fear, knowing their cousin's demise was on their hands because of their deeds. That is a pain you cannot be freed from.

Disguised as a less fortunate individual, my uncle felt he was ready. Marian Sandmaier cites, "A sibling may be the keeper of one's identity, the only person with the keys to one's unfettered, more fundamental self." To kill the prospect would supply a sense of comfort to my father by the ways of my uncle's doing, but it would also allow my uncle to free himself of the agony of not being at his brother's aid during that time. So, it all worked out in the way it should have.

People tend to neglect the less fortunate, as if they do not exist. Every night, the prospect would walk over to the liquor store around the corner from where he lived. As he would leave out of his back door, he would see a man who he thought was just someone living on the street. Just another homeless man who found that spot to be his safe haven. So he never put much thought to it, which is quite common in Chicago; the population is shocking. Over five thousand people are homeless, some even veterans and the youth. So blending in would have been effortless. The prospect walked by my uncle, whose back was toward him, and never once acknowledged him sitting there. If he did, he would have been more aware of his surroundings, because by now, my uncle was on his feet, following the path of the prospect. The prospect never once looked back. My uncle came from behind, gripping him around the neck, allowing his body to collapse from a rear chokehold. My uncle released his grip, as he was not trying to kill; he just needed him to take a nap. It only lasted for a second, then he regained consciousness, but within those few seconds, my uncle was able to do what had to be done.

He tied him down and taped his mouth shut to keep him quiet. By the time the prospect woke up, he found himself bound in the trunk of my uncle's throwaway car and being driven to an abandoned church on Sixty-Ninth and Steward. Once there, my uncle walked the prospect down to the basement of the church. A basement of an abandoned building, dark and chilly, city rodents running rampant. You may hear voices, but there are none. It's all in your head. I cannot put into words the thoughts that were in the head of the prospect because I do not know what he was thinking, but he earnestly pleaded for his life as the tape was removed from his mouth. It wasn't long before the tape went back around his mouth for talking too much, my uncle said.

Prior to leaving, my uncle reached into the pockets of the prospect and took everything he had—motorcycle keys, wallet, a few fruities he had but he dropped those on the ground; he did not want any candy. Once he got what he needed, my uncle walked out from the basement, leaving the prospect alone. If an opportunity presented itself, I am sure he could have escaped, but, tightly bound, there was no way for him to walk up some steps then somehow open the door to the outside. If he did, good for him.

Little time had passed when my uncle returned. He pulled up to the church riding on the prospect's motorcycle. If the prospect was still there, tied down in the basement, he would have heard the roaring sounds of the motorcycle, but then it went silent. The basement doors opened and he heard footsteps and steel tow chains thump the floor of each step. My uncle came out of the dark, hovering over the prospect as he lay there, bound and gagged. The prospect was stripped down. No shirt, no pants, no socks, no shoes, no underwear. Fully nude. He was hogtied as if he were a pig. Wrists attached to the ankles, held together by metal chains, back arched, face in the upward position. He was too heavy to carry, so my uncle dragged the prospect's body up the flight of stairs to the outside.

With the prospect still in the same hog-tied position, my uncle wrapped the hooks of the tow chain attached to the prospect around the metal frame of the motorcycle. The prospect was unprotected; his torso, thighs, and genitals were the only portions of his body that touched the cold surface of the asphalt. My uncle made sure his face was unscratched. The prospect needed to be recognizable to his friends and family. Once the body was fastened, it was time to go. Usually around two to three a.m., it is typically criminals, streetwalkers, and tricks out. Even so, my uncle did not care; they were going for that last ride. Chicago to Joliet was around forty-five miles apart, give or take, which is about an hour's drive.

He took I-55 South and rode as fast as the bike allowed.

Arriving in Joliet, he drove to the home of the prospect's parents. His flesh was visible, skin was torn from his body from every mile that was driven. Genitals were gone. The prospect died on the road. My uncle unchained the prospect from the bike and dragged the body onto the lawn of the parents' home. He positioned the body like a garden ornament in the direction of the front door. Whoever walked out of the home first would see the face of the prospect.

That following morning, the death of the prospect was broadcasted on every news channel. There were no potential suspects, but people wondered how someone could be so heartless to leave the decimated body of the son on the front lawn of his parents. It was an ungodly act. The parents came forward and pleaded with the public to help find this ferocious bastard who had tortured their child.

No one knew the truth behind my uncle's act. Never once did he avow nor tell Lil Stace or my father that he was the one who committed that offense. I am sure they had their suspicions, but they never talked about it. It was a conversation that did not need to be explored. Knowing what happened would not have made a difference. It was handled. After the death of the prospect, my father kept a relationship with the sister. He felt that giving her a child would be a good trade-off for the death of her brother due to the hands of his brother. That was fair. So, here am I, Alexander Lee Jr. Born from sins of murder, lies, and molestation, this is the exegesis of the biblical phrase "born of sin."

CHAPTER THREE

Son of the Morning

Time moved on since the death of my father, but because of what I saw, my mother felt it would be best to have me homeschooled. She never did care for public school to begin with. The elementary school I attended told my mother they needed to run testing on me because I was not like the other students. I didn't understand the material they were teaching, nor was I paying attention to what they were teaching. I found class to be uninspiring. Because of the way they were teaching, my mother felt it was tied to the devil's dealing. They teach you how to think like everyone else, then label you as something else when you think freely. So, they held me back for a year.

A book I once read was called *Outwitting the Devil* by Napoleon Hill. In this body of work, Napoleon Hill creates a fictious interview between himself and the Devil, but refers to the Devil as "Your Majesty." It was designed as a Q&A of truths. Hill asks a question and Your Majesty enlightens with the truth. Hill asks, "Never mind about me, tell me about this second best trick of yours with which you induce people to drift with you to hell." Your Majesty responds, "My second best trick is not second at all. It is first! It is first because without it I never could gain control of the minds of the youths. Parents, schoolteachers, religious instructors, and many other adults unknowingly serve my purpose by helping me to destroy in children the habit of thinking for themselves. They go about their work in various ways, never suspecting what they are doing to the minds of children or the real cause of the children's mistakes."

I found that to be interesting. As you study life and people, you tend to see the world differently. To that response, I found that to be true. Sitting in the church, the pastor called the children of the congregation to come sit in the front. As you watched the body language of the pastor, it changed from his normal presentation stance. As you paid close attention to the levels of his voice, they became softer. He aggressively moved forward in a very docile way, but consciously, he was aware of what he was doing, concealing his intentions. Control the mind. Outside of a church, parents tend to hinder their child's growth by being overprotective. By helping your child more than needed, your child loses their self-confidence.

My mother was an evil woman, strong-minded, intelligent, but also extremely dangerous. Prophet Muhammad said, "Heaven lies at the feet of your mother." I did not receive peace, love, and happiness from my mother. I experienced much worse growing up under her supervision. Abandonment and the feeling of being unloved, it saddens anyone to feel that, but for a child, it can create a level of hatred and the desire to seek attention from elsewhere.

Sheltered from the outside world, I did not have friends nor did I have family, just my mom. In our home, we had a back room that allowed no outside light to shine in, the size of single-man cell. It was built in a similar way—cold, concrete floors, tainted white walls, one metal bucket that sat in the far-right corner of the room, no mattress but a desk with a lamp. I also had my room across the hall that I would sleep in at night. Bedtime was at 8:30 p.m., but I had to be up at 5:00 a.m. That was my routine—wake up, shower, have breakfast, which I ate in the back room just as I did with my other meals. I stayed in the back room from 6:00 a.m. until 8:00 p.m., then I would go shower then to bed. I did have a clock; my mother wanted to make sure I knew the time. She made sure I understood time too. Time is mathematics in life. Using the twenty-four-hour gauge is how we use our time, noble and glorious. She made sure I stayed hydrated; I had lots of water. My meals were persistently handed to me at the same time each day. Three meals a day with snacks, such as fruit, in between each meal. I learned how to space out my hunger. The days my mother would go out, she would prep my meals and give them to me all at once. Fourteen hours a day in a room, you would eat each meal within the first three hours. After a few nights of going to bed hungry, I consumed only small portions. Having control over my hunger was the first component of being self-disciplined. If I could control when I ate and what I ate, I could then control everything else involving myself. The way I strengthened that discipline was by fasting weekly or whenever I felt myself being weak-minded. That carried into my adult life.

Her style of learning—teaching—was unconventional, but it worked for me. It taught me how to use my imagination, be resourceful and spirited. The creative adult is the child who survived. I read and wrote each day. My mother gave me black ballpoint pens, yellow highlighters, a flashlight, a spiral notepad, a dictionary, and books on diverse topics. She made sure I read and drafted a book report on each novel, creating my own summary of what I learned by reading that individual book. Each book was like a best friend I never had. I explored a different world alongside each character. We went on voyages together. Flying with a black-headed seagull over Gullah Gullah Island, prowling through Buckingham Palace in London with bloodthirsty vampires, walking around in the district with my sociopath hound as we schemed on our family, dying in the arms of war on the streets of Oakland with my brother "Lil Bobby," whose real name was Robert James Hutton, or as I marched on Washington, standing next to my fellow brother as he delivered his speech at the Lincoln Memorial: "I have a DREAM." See, I would rather walk with a friend in the dark than walk alone in the light.

When I closed my eyes at night, I pretended I was lying across the lawn, looking into the galaxy as the stars illuminated the sky, as if my father were saying, "Hi, son." All I had was my greatest resource that all humans have—the mind. I studied, I read, and I wrote. My personal writings became my fantasies. A story about a child named Rozak, titled, "The Life of Rozak," was the first story I wrote when I would have been in the third grade. The story was about crime, family, and escapism. Rozak was a fine young boy who understood what family meant. Born in Turkey, a Middle Eastern country, he was the oldest of three. Rozak had a brother who was seven and a sister who was nine.

They lived in a house with a single parent, their father deceased because of chronic obstructive pulmonary disease. Being the oldest, Rozak held the biggest responsibility of looking after his siblings while his mom tried to make ends meet. Occasionally she would go on dates with men. She knew her kids needed a fatherly figure in the house to provide fatherly structure.

The mother was dating a wealthy man who worked within the government. The interactions with Rozak and this man were rare. He only came around a few times. The mother was not ready for him to meet all her kids, but Rozak went to this man's home with his mom to pick up some food that he arranged for her and the family. The mother went on a date with that man one night but never made it back home. Rozak knew she was going out with him. He knew of her company but not her whereabouts. The following morning, the sister turned on the television to reveal a news story about a body found a few miles away from their home. It was their mother. Rozak had a suspicion that her date would know something about his mother's death.

As the kids gathered in the living room, knocks sounded on the front door. The police made themselves known. Rozak knew that if he were to answer the door, his family would have been taken into custody because their only guardian was now dead. With the TV off, room silent, Rozak waited for the officer to leave. Once he left, Rozak knew he needed an answer as to why his mom was dead. He told his siblings to sit tight and to not answer the door for anyone.

That night, Rozak went over to that man's house. He knocked on the door, but there was no answer. Rozak was a clever child, so he found a way through a back door that entered the home. Once inside, Rozak waited patiently for the arrival of the homeowner. Hours went by until a car finally pulled into the driveway. Rozak overheard chatter as someone approached the door. It was not just one voice. It was two. From the sounds of it, the man had a female companion with him. But Rozak had a baseball bat with him. Once the door opened, the lights were turned on. The man jumped, the lady screamed—both frightened, both caught off guard—they had not expected to find anyone, let alone Rozak, sitting in the middle of the room. But they did.

Rozak advised the woman that it would be in her best interests to leave. As she did, the man closed the door behind her. Rozak demanded that the man take a seat on the couch. Rozak rose to his feet and paced back and forth. He dragged the bat across the floor, creating an anxiety in the man of not knowing what would happen next. The man began to speak.

"Why are you doing this, why are you here?"

"Why did you kill my mom?" Rozak replied. The man played innocent, but his behavior showed differently.

"Who was that woman?" Rozak asked. The man disregarded the questions as he begged for his life. Rozak became annoyed with the man's presence. He continued to pace the room. As he walked behind the man, the man stood up. Rozak cracked the side of the man's kneecap with the bat as he tried to stand on his feet. Letting out a cry of pain, the man curled into the fetal position and covered his head. Rozak eventually broke the grip and split the back of the man's head. As his blood poured out, Rozak did not stop; he kept swinging until his arms grew tired. The man's face was no longer identifiable.

Rozak went into the man's garage in search of something flammable but did not know what to use, so instead he turned the man's oven on then walked over and set the living room curtains on fire. As Rozak walked out of the front door, the flames went into an uproar. The following morning, Rozak became a suspect to the local police for the death of a government official. The beautiful lady had gone to the police and given a full report of what she saw. Rozak knew he had to go. A man who had been close to his father helped Rozak do just that. That friend was able to get Rozak and his siblings across the country to New York. Once in the Big Apple, Rozak began to work as a soldier for the mob. Rozak grew through the ranks and became an acting boss for that mob. He eventually got arrested and convicted of killing an NYPD government official, but the truth behind the story was that it was a frame job. That was the first story I wrote as a child.

Most of my writings were built on realities and fantasies. The fantasy was not for me to escape, but it allowed me to survive my reality. The reality of my life was no different than yours. We all have our phases, our stories, when we go through our trial moments in our lives, which provide us the tools to survive in our reality.

One trial moment in my life happened just before my ninth birthday. That night before my birthday was when I became mindful of what my mother was truly capable of and the rootwork that she practiced religiously. Never once had I met a woman who was gorgeous, intelligent, a woman who believed in something she could not see, but my mother's character was far worse than Mephistopheles, a demon in German folklore. That night, she took me on a two-hour drive from our home to Streator, Illinois, about 101 miles from where we lived. Throughout the ride there, we sat in silence; she never mentioned where we were headed, nor did I ask. We stopped at a secluded site in the middle of nowhere. There were a few parked cars, but besides that, it was nothing but clear skies, open land, and trees. After we had arrived, she told me to get out and follow her. As I did, we walked for what seemed like a mile. Butterflies rattled in my stomach; I felt scared of the uncertainty of what was to come, but I also felt protected because I was with my mom. She was my protector. I trusted her. But what was to come was something no child or human being should have to go through. As we came closer to the circle, I noticed seven candles, blankets, a handbasket, a bucket, a group of four people, and a goat. Making eye contact with the goat sent chills, a tingling, cold brain-wave feeling in my mind. The seventh candle was the torch that sat between the horns of the goat, its flame reflected on the goat's tiny gold-colored marble eyes, revealing its true devilish features. Her right hoof was picking at the black collar fastened around her neck. I was more afraid of the goat than she was of me. I felt sweat dripping off my lower back. My legs became weak as I took each step. I had to hold the arm of my mother as we walked in step to control my balance.

As my mom and I walked toward the group of four who were dressed in white robes, each wearing a black-and-white-checkered masquerade mask with a long, gold pigeon nose, I felt piss creep down my inner thigh. It was like something out of a movie. Like when a scary clown comes out of nowhere and jumps in your face. The instant shock. I couldn't hold it in. I started to grow scared. The blowing of the trees didn't help. I silently pleaded for help. I called out for my father. I spoke his name twice; the first time I said his name was in my head, and I repeated it to myself, but this time I spoke with conviction. I needed to be heard. So, I spoke his name out loud. My mother looked at me with hatred. She hated the fact I called for my father. The man she had killed. What hindered her from lashing out at me was her respect for the ceremony. She was the host and I was the guest of honor. This was my birthday party.

One of the men asked if I was ready; my mom replied "yes." The man said, "We will get in formation." He then walked off along with the other two men and the woman. The formation was a couple of feet from where we were. They stood in a wide, cross-like position. The men were in the north, west, and south positions as the woman stood at the east. They proceeded to walk outward in their respective directions to give a wide enough space in the formation. My mother took off my shirt and then got down on her knees to unfasten my jeans. While I stood in my underwear, my mother rose to her feet and disrobed. That was the first time I had seen my mother nude, but not the first time I had seen a naked woman. When I was five years old, my uncle locked me in a room and had me watch ebony porn. He did not want me to grow up to be gay or have a sexual attraction to men. He wanted my sexual attention to be toward women. Watch and learn. Exploiting a woman's sexual desires and satisfying her needs could make her weak, which will ultimately give you control over her mind. And she will do everything for you. It is the power of manipulation through sex. So, being able to see a naked woman—whether my mother or not my mother—it was surprising because I had never actually seen it live or in person. My mother was a petite woman with long, curly hair that fell to her lower back, a peanut-butter complexion, small perky breasts, and a bush that covered her kitty. She walked over to a metal bucket that seemed to be filled with water and bathed herself before putting on the black robe. Once finished, she walked over to me and announced that phase one was to begin.

The voices of everyone became louder as we approached the formation. The candles were lit, the goat was set aside, and everyone started to sing as the ritual began. My mother guided me over to the man who sat at the north. As the two spoke in tongues, my mother held my hand as we advanced around the formation. Each member was able to physically discipline me in their own way as we marched around the formation. A smack on the chest, abdomen, back, anywhere but the face. The pain level increased as we toured through each path. After the third travel around the formation, we stopped in the south where one of the men stood. My mother and he began to speak in tongues. Reaching into his robe pocket, he exposed a syringe as he delivered his dialogue and told me to open my mouth and to take it all. As he gushed the fluid into my mouth, it tasted like honey. It did not end there. We began the journey once more. The group continued to chant in hymns as I made my way from one path to another, escorted by my mother. This time, we went around twice instead of three times, as we did before. We came to a halt at the west, and just like the man in the south, he and my mother began to recite their cadence to each other. He took out a syringe and had me drink the contents. The fluid that was rushed down my throat had a bitter taste, vinegar. One last tour around the formation as we came to a standstill in the east; the woman and my mother began to speak in tongues. My mother announced that phase one was completed.

Phase two began as my mother and the woman continued to speak in tongues. I was forced to extend my arm and hold the hand of the woman in the east as my mother went to go and collect the goat so we could move forward with the ceremony. The closer the goat got, the more you could see of its devilish features. My mother walked the goat into the inner section of the formation as the woman released her grip on my hand. With her hand pressed on my shoulder, she directed me over to my mother and the goat. The chanting of hymns would be present until the act was done. The woman reached into her pocket and handed me a sticking knife. She removed herself from the inner circle and returned to her post. My mother looked over at me and nodded her head as if I knew what to do. I reached over, taking the leash from my mother, and wrapped it around the palm of my hand. I mounted myself on the back of the goat and pulled back its horns with the same hand that held on to her leash—my right hand. The chanting became louder and louder as the last moments were coming to an end.

My mother spoke, "May you receive power and riches, wisdom and strength, honor and glory, and the blessings of the gods will be in your favor." I instantly drew the knife across its throat from ear to ear, hearing the cries of the goat as its soul left its body and the chants grew louder. The feeling of blood coating my left hand brought memories of my father's death to my mind, when my hands were covered in his blood. I instantly dropped the knife, looked down, and saw that I was saturated in the goat's blood. I became lost, stuck in a daze. My mother announced the completion of phase two.

Phase three was to begin now. As the night grew colder and the skies darkened, the push of the wind was powerful enough to rattle the trees. The stars did not give off much light. My inner voices cried out for help, but they were not loud enough. I looked up to see if my father would come down from the heavens, but that was merely a wishful thought. A cold wet cloth came down on my face as my mother washed me down to prepare me for the closing chapter of the ritual. Removing my undergarments, I stood nude in front of my mother. As the cloth brushed over my genital area, a tear fell down my face. My mother rose to her feet, disrobing herself. As the robe fell off her shoulders onto the ground, my mother stood there in front of me as naked as I. We stared at each other as the woman standing in the east came from behind my mother, her robe no longer on her back.

I looked around and everyone was naked. Robes cast onto the ground. I did not have any thoughts. I stood there watching as the lady's hand eased her way down my mother's bare body, one hand around her neck and the other hand down between my mother's thighs. I watched as my mother fell into a form of paradise from sexual interactions with another woman, as I felt a rough, wet finger position inside my rectum. I could not move. I felt my heart pound in my ears and grow faster and faster. My hands began to sweat and shake as the man touched me. As he inserted another finger inside me, my breath became so fast that my vision darkened at the motions of his hand.

The woman and my mother drifted away from us. My mother lay down on her back as the woman's face disappeared between my mother's thighs. The finger began to go deeper inside me. The man whispered in my ear, with his other hand on my shoulder directing me onto my stomach. I felt his hand press down on my lower back while the head of his cock pierced my anal cavity, stretching me as wide as the girth of his cock. There was no point in fighting it. It would have made things worse. These men would have overpowered me, held me down on each arm, and still would have pushed inside me. I just had to accept that. I began to scream as tears poured down my face. The pain was something I had never felt before. He thrust and thrust and the deeper he went, the more it hurt. I turned my head, looking over at my mother as she was fully engaged with the woman. I turned my head in the opposite direction and stared into the dark. After the first man was done, the second one came behind me. He was full force; his motions were faster and harder than the first man's. By the time the third man was inside me, I had become numb. Once he got off of me, I rolled onto my side, putting my hands underneath me as I silently cried myself to sleep.

The following morning, I rose to the sun. My mother sat cross-legged as I was the last to awake. I looked around and saw that everyone was gone. The candles, blankets, and the goat were gone as well. My mother said, "Come on, let's go home," and picked up my clothing and started to get dressed. Every time I squeezed my cheeks, I felt a discomfort. But I could not help it; I kept squeezing to feel the irritating pain. Once in the car, we drove home in silence. Never once did she ask how it was, how I was, nor did she say she loved me. No words were spoken. Just muteness all the way home.

Arriving home, we pulled into the driveway. My mother put the car in park and told me to look at her as she said, "I want you to go inside and take a cold bath to clean yourself off." I just nodded my head yes. She said, "Lock the door behind you." My mother then exited the car and headed inside the house, never looking back at me, but I waited in hopes that my mother would come back out and ask me what's wrong. More importantly, I just wanted her to tell me she loved me. She never did.

I eventually got out the car and walked into my home, passing my mother's room, the door closed. Not all the way but slightly cracked. At that moment, I cried. A mother's hug could have saved me. I wanted my father. I wanted to feel like a nine-year-old kid receiving his first gaming console. I wanted to feel, but I felt nothing.

I gathered some clothes from my room along with my towel to take a bath and went into the bathroom and shut the door. I ran the bath water at a cold temperature, like my mother told me to do. As the water began to rise, I began to undress. My shirt came off first, then I nervously took off my pants and undergarments. Dried crusts of semen stuck to my inner thigh. Too afraid to look at myself in the mirror or use the bathroom, I went to sit down in the tub, but immediately stood up from the discomfort of the cold water as it wet the crack of my ass. I turned on the shower toggle, allowing the water to splash against my face. I grabbed the soap and cleaned every inch of my body as tears came down my face. The tears finally stopped; it could have been from the water, but it was not. No more tears, no more pain. A moment of clarity. This is where I understood that I was no longer the son of my mother. She gave me up at the ritual to a higher power.

As I came out of the shower to dry myself, towel wrapped around my waist, I used my hand to clean off the bathroom mirror from the steam, took a long look at myself in the mirror, and felt emotionlessness. I stood still. A halo swept the room, sending an influential feeling to satisfy a need that was needed. I wanted to kill my mother. I wished a tear, or something, would have appeared that would have influenced me to go give her a hug and kiss, tell her I loved her. But when I tended to wish, my wishes never came to fruition. The wish of being loved by my mother, the wish of seeing my father again, the wish that my uncle had saved me from being molested, the wish of removing the images from my mind of my mother shooting my father, the wish of not having my father's blood on my hands, the wish of having a better life as child. I gave up on wishing. We do not decide on the tools that are used to shape who we become. My mother birthed a monster. She witnessed firsthand what she had created.

I pressed open my mother's door and watched as she lay there, covers off to the side, her body fully bare, just like last night. She was beautiful, skin glowing. My mother was a goddess. I saw why my father fell head over heels for her. She believed in vibrations, spirits, a higher power. She believed in faith. That was that woman, but she was wicked.

I knew where my mother hid her gun—in the upper drawer of her dresser. It was a loaded .38 special revolver. I closed the drawer and walked over to the wicker chair that was in her direct eyesight. I sat. I waited for her to wake. There was an incommunicable feeling that needed to be fulfilled. I heard soft-toned voices that spoke to me. *Kill her, kill her, kill her, or she'll kill you, she doesn't love, she hates you.* My thoughts became out of control, unable to sort out as the visions of the death of my father, the abuse I had taken over the years from my mother, being sodomized by a group of men all surfaced in a child's mind—my mind. Those moments I came up against, suffered, stemmed a level of hatred she had created. The fact that she did not love me anymore. That she chose her life, her practices, her faith over her child was the driving factor to my commitment.

I was fully aware and in the moment. I did not want to wake her out of her sleep. I was patient until she woke. She started to toss and turn. At that point, I knew whatever was going to happen was going happen. One of us had to go. *It will be her then me,* I thought. The suffering — the pain — it would all be over with then. I could live with that, but there is no coming back from killing your own mother. I had to come to an agreement with myself to follow with my action. I knew her death would be why I would walk this world alone. Where I would have no one to take me to school, pack my lunch, hug and hold me, tell me they love me.

My mother awoke and acknowledged my presence as I sat across from her. She said, "What are you doing?" She noticed the gun in my lap as I rose to my feet. I remained silent until I told her to roll over onto her stomach. She followed my orders and did precisely that. As I moved toward my mother, the towel around my waist dropped to the floor. I stood naked in front of my mother as she turned over to put her face in the mattress. Once she was facedown, I mounted myself on top of her. Her body was between my legs. She did not give me a fight nor a plea for her life. She wanted this. In a way, she was exhausted from the life she lived, but felt honored knowing her baby boy was growing into a man. Her ways of teaching had forged a dangerous mind.

She spoke, saying, "I am proud of you, Alexander Lee Jr. But this is who we are, son. I say this from the deepest, purest part of my heart — I love you." I hesitated. Unsure if I could commit to this act. She felt the nervousness in me. She had said the words I had been yearning to hear. She said she loved me. But I knew better, and so did she. She encouraged me to follow through with my plan.

"I'm ready," she said.

She turned her face, staring into the bedroom mirror. She murmured to herself how beautiful she looked and told me to never stop believing. I proceeded to grab the pillow with my left hand, hovering it over her head. I, too, looked in the mirror before covering her face. I was the last face she would see. I placed the pillow on top of her head as she had done to my father, pressed the barrel of the .38 special into the pillow, inhaled a deep breath, pulled the trigger back, and fired two bullets into the pillow. Then, I exhaled. I looked up, looked around the room, caught my own reflection in the mirror. I could not see myself as the innocent child with chubby cheeks and curly hair anymore. I nodded my head, accepting what I had just done. Without thinking, I turned the .38 special on me and pulled the trigger. But it only sounded with a single *click*. Out of curiosity, I pulled again and, once again, nothing but the sound of a *click*. The gun was jammed or empty. I was confused as to why it did not go off. Was it a sign? Whatever the reason, I did not know it at that time, but every ending is also a new beginning.

CHAPTER FOUR

He Is I, I Am Him

I packed my bookbag as light as possible, only taking what was needed as I embarked on a voyage I knew nothing about. At the age of nine, I had no idea how I was going to survive. But I coped. The lessons I had learned would always be rooted in me. We are who we are by the byproduct of all of our lessons.

When I left home, all I took was an outfit, a pen, a pad, a highlighter, a pocketknife, a few apples and oranges, the .38 special, a Bible, and my small green stuffed animal, Journi. That is all I felt I would need. But what I was going to eat, where I was going to sleep, that I did not know. So I began my travels. The more steps I took, the bigger the test became. It was hard, but I figured it out. When it came to food, my father had a friend who worked in small convenience store who would allow me to take whatever I wanted and warm up food whenever I needed. I would wash up every morning using water I kept from the previous day to wash my face and brush my teeth. Around the city, there were abandoned buildings, boarded-up homes. Some nights were cooler than others. Every night, I would fall asleep to the sounds of gunfire, dogs barking, police sirens, any kind of noise—I heard it all. The noise helped me sleep at night. Some nights, I would sleep at the same building, and some nights, I would not. Each location I slept at gave a unique experience than the one before. Some nights would be quiet; I could sleep the night away. But those were few. Most nights, I wrestled with images of my mother's and father's deaths. I thought about each stroke of those men as they pushed inside me. Too young to tell, but I have questioned my sexuality since.

Chicago Public Library became my safe haven. The majority of my day would be spent there. Just reading books of all kinds—some even in a foreign language. I taught myself how to speak Turkish. Whatever I could do to keep my mind engaged, I would do it. I read on how allowing yourself to be immersed in the beauty of nature—by watching flowers grow, birds chat, the simple stuff—it all could provide serenity. By allowing yourself to live in the moment, you realize the beauty the world has to offer outside of the pain and the struggles we try so hard to get out of. Not knowing that pain leaves a gift behind, we tend to allow ourselves to be stuck in our own world. So, we do not see it. We're unable to understand the good in a dire situation. I go to the bookshelf in my mind and reflect on the times when I was sheltered away from the outside world with no TV. Locked in a backroom with only a pen, books, and a notepad. It allowed me to discover my creative gift and the passion I have for writing.

For a nine-year-old, I became advanced for my age. I may not be able to identify what the Pythagorean theorem is or if I mix two chemicals together, what would be the reaction, but if I want to learn how to blow something up or add and subtract numbers, I can do that. What I was learning, school could not teach. I was learning how to survive and make use of the tools I was given. Whenever I would feel overwhelmed by my studies or needed some air, I would go for a walk behind the library. It had a mile-long trail that looped around from start to finish. I walked that trail every day. Occasionally twice a day, depending on my attitude. The trail was refreshing, therapeutic for me. I could clear my mind, home in on the lessons I had learned from my studies. It provided what seemed to be missing from my life—peace. Halfway through the trail was a bench called "Edith." That was my resting spot. Sometimes I would sit and speak aloud to the heavens above. As I was sitting down one day, a random homeless man came and asked if he could sit next to me. Blond hair, blue eyes, a white man. He was short and carried a sign that read, "I Tried," which, to me, was interesting. So, I told him sure. He introduced himself as GM, which was the abbreviation to his name. I then told him it was a pleasure to meet him, and introduced myself as Alexander Lee Jr.

I remember reading a quote by William Butler Yeats that reads, "There are no strangers here; only friends you haven't met yet." The strangers I've met in my life played a part in my story; our experiences we shared together is what allowed me to call them friends. GM was no different from the ones I met later in my life or before. He was a friend I was meant to meet; it just took some time for me to get to him. But as he sat next to me, he asked if I was hungry. I told him, "I'm starving, sir. Cheese and crackers are the only thing I have eaten so far." So, he offered me his turkey sandwich. Told me to have it. He said where he was going, he wouldn't need it.

He asked me how I was doing. He said, "I see you walk this trail every day as I watch from a distance." He said he never wanted to come out in the open because it gives a discomfort to the ones who walk the trail.

"People tend to become weirdos when a brother or sister from the less privileged is in their existence. They feel as if they are not people like them," he said. As I ate, I listened as GM told me his story of how he became homeless. It was unfortunate, but he stood on top of it. He never passed the buck to blame someone else for his shortcomings.

A man who once lived the white American's dream, he graduated high school, went to college, and earned a bachelor degree in business. He established himself at a well-paying position in a tech company and he built a family of his own—had a wife, a kid, and a dog. His house had the white picket fence with beautiful green grass— "Something out of a magazine," he expressed. He lived the life that society tries to paint for you. Follow those steps and you will have that. Which he did, but the more I listened, the deeper his story became. A young man at the age of thirty-eight who grew up having everything given to him and never had to struggle to the point where he had to find himself. "Life was easy," he proclaimed. One day, he was fixing up his home. As he was adding crystals around his chandelier, his foot slipped off the ladder, he lost his balance, and he found his heel pressed to the back of his thigh.

The doctors prescribed him painkillers until they felt he was okay, that he no longer needed the medication. That the pain was no longer present. But he was now at a point where he was chasing a high. That chase eventually led to losing everything he had gained—his house, job, family. He drained his bank account to support his habit. Used every drug that the streets would offer; he was searching for that fix.

GM went to jail for stealing electronics for dope dealers—stealing a laptop in exchange for dope. But through all that, it led him to sit next to me on the bench. So I asked him, "Where you going now?"

He said, "I want to be a better man, and in doing so, there are steps I have to take, and my first step is to seek help." He continued, "There is a program called Windy City Rescue Mission. It's a foundation to help provide shelter along with help to develop tools for us to become better men and women. I go in today; they have a bed for me." As he stood up, he handed me a cassette player with headphones. Told me to have it, that it was a gift from him to me. He said, "It helped me get through my journey, and it could do the same for you."

I said, "Thank you, sir."

Before he walked off, he added, "When you see men fall, do not laugh. Learn. I love you, kid," and then he walked away.

I put on the headset and watched as he strolled off. De La Soul began to play in the cassette player. The first song it played was "Me Myself and I." Everything at that moment felt right. I was vibing to the sounds of De La

Soul. It was a feel-good feeling. I stood on my feet, prowled on the trail, skipping, two-stepping—I was just taking it all in. I did not see nobody but me out there. I felt like a kid.

Along the trail, there were no outside restrooms, so I had to go back inside the library. The bathrooms were on the lower level, which was also down in the basement and TV area. As I came out of the bathroom, there was a TV show airing: the K. Wynn afternoon talk show. The segment of the show was called "Black Butterfly." What really caught my attention was when I heard the guest on the show say, "The light only shines through those people who have cracked."

The guest on the show was a man named Darren. He was a young, inspiring African American brother. The more and more I listened to him speak, the more I realized we both had similar pasts growing up. Mr. K. Wynn told him, "Tell us your story, Darren." Mr. K. Wynn said that when he first heard Darren's story, it reminded him of the Book of Job from the Bible.

Darren began to talk about his life's journey. He started off by saying, "Your past just gives you permission to be in your present." This man dropped out of high school his junior year. He was not raised by a poor family and didn't live in a bad area; he was not hood or street. At the age of nine, he started drinking, smoking, playing with guns, dating women almost twice his age, but his uncle steered him away from that. He introduced Darren to sports— basketball, football, wrestling, and modeling. He even played in a celebrity basketball game. So, that is what he did growing up. He just did not make the best choices his freshman year of high school. But when you take that one thing away from someone, they just find something else to replace it. So what do you expect a black teenager to do when you take that one thing away? His mother worked to provide, his father was not around, his cousin was a gangster, his uncle could not teach anything outside of sports or how to meet women. Darren mentioned when it came to sports and women, he wasn't good at either. He was honest about himself.

The day before he started losing his way, he was a basketball player. Not the best, but it kept him away from the nonsense. The best game he played was the night before he got kicked off the team. The administration of the school athletics department did not like how he conducted himself the night before. He led that game as the leading scorer with the most rebounds and had a few assists, but the way he reacted to the opposing team was unsportsmanlike. He tried to bang on a rival teammate. The kid defending Darren could not manage his ability, so he played dirty. Poking his side in post. Just foul sportsmanship. Once the game ended, that same player gave Darren a shoulder check as they walked past to shake hands. Darren turned around and forcefully responded by shoving him down on his face. Next day, he and two teammates were kicked off the team. A friend who lived around the corner from his great-grandmother, who he grew up with, came to him and they sat in the garage. His friend asked him if he wanted to sell some bags of weed. This friend's father had given him an ounce of weed.

Darren said, "Why not?" He had just been kicked off the basketball team, so he did not have much else going on. His friend gave him a hundred dollars' worth of weed to sell the following day at school, and Darren did just that. All the bags were sold within the first class period or two. Darren kept fifty dollars and gave the other man his share.

Darren fell in love with the hustle. He started earning, building his customer base from students to teachers, and he felt it was no use to attend high school anymore. So, he dropped out. Started robbing people, committing home invasions. The deeper he fell, the deeper it got. He started by selling weed and ended up being asked to murder for capital gain.

The story about his life became more interesting because the turning point in his life was monumental. It started when he was considering committing suicide on Christmas Eve. He said he had a .357 magnum revolver and he was ready. He was tired. Tired from the wrongs he had done, which got him nothing but misery. Tired of the continuous battle he had within. He had his own insecurities with how he perceived himself. But he thought of his family, his niece. He knew suicide was a coward's way of going out. In a way, that could have been the reason that stopped him that night. But that following week, his life was saved when SWAT raided his mother's home. When they arrived, Darren was sleeping. He heard his sister's voice saying, "Mom, police is at the door." Then *boom*, the door was kicked in. They ran up the stairs. Darren hurried out of bed, but before he could do anything, there were three officers all aiming M-16s right at his forehead. His family was there in the living room watching it all take place. One aggressive move on Darren's part and they would have shot him.

They were told that Darren had guns in the house and that was the first thing they asked for when he was put in handcuffs. His family watched as he was escorted out of their home. During that interview, Darren became emotional, as he thought this was the last time he physically saw and heard his grandmother's voice. The thing he remembered her saying was, "Can he put some shoes on his feet?"

Mr. K. Wynn asked, "Did they allow it?"

Darren said, "They did."

His grandmother died two months later from breast cancer. Being locked up has its moments, but one of the most challenging parts is when you get a visit from a family member or friend. There are mixed emotions in the room. Pain and joy. The joy of being able to talk with ones that love you, but the pain of knowing the damage that you had caused. More importantly, the hurt that you feel when they walk out the room. You watch from your cell window as they get in their car and drive off. Then again, you can receive a letter or a phone call saying that a close relative or two had died. Darren found out his grandmother had passed—"GG went to heaven," his niece said—from a conversation he had with his niece over the phone in the county jail.

As Darren was escorted into the police car, he watched his uncle race down the street. As soon as his uncle parked, the police forced his uncle on the ground, knees buried in the snow. Darren and he locked eyes. Darren said, "At that moment, that's when I knew I let him down. That is what hurt the most. It was not that I was about to be sent away for some time. That did not bother me. The police raiding my mother's home, finding guns and drugs, that did not bother me. Being set up, because someone had to have told the police, that did not bother me. But watching my uncle on his knees because of my wrongdoings, that's what bothered me."

Darren's story kept rolling, how he faced a Class X charge of armed violence that carried up to thirty years. The judge offered him twenty years at the age of twenty at eighty-five percent. He was offered more time than the man who murdered his cousin two months after his arrest. During Darren's stay, he lost his grandma from cancer and his cousin was killed from a shotgun wound to the head—his death was street related. Darren talked about how an inmate tried to label him as a snitch for something he never said or did. So, he had to sit down with certain men and explain himself, show paperwork of his case. Darren sat down with men who were in there for murder, men who ran shit, but it worked in his favor. He had men who were ready to go to war for him, all because when his back was against the wall, he held his ground. Darren never once snitched. He was respected and protected on the yards he walked on. He was an individual before he went to prison—trying to be something you're not will get you hurt. He never once acted hard, stated he was from Bolingbrook but he owned his shit. He respected himself and everyone around him. He governed himself accordingly. When you speak, "Yes sir, no sir." When you walk past someone, "Excuse me sir." He learned what respect was. Prison taught him that.

Leaving visitation from seeing his attorney, Darren went back to his cell and prayed. That same week his attorney came back and told him that if he pled guilty, they would lower his charge to a Class 1. They offered Darren boot camp on top of eight years. Boot camp was a four-to-six-month program, but if you failed to complete the program, you would have to go and do the time you were given. Darren was given the max of eight years but he could get out of boot camp in four months, or six months if they had to extend it due to his behavior. Darren completed the program in four months. He did a total of ten months from being held at Will County, shipped off to Stateville and Vienna, and finished his term at Dixon Springs Boot Camp. That was when he knew the power of prayer. Prison was a blessing for him. God will use an enemy to get you to your destiny. Prison was Darren's enemy.

The TV instantly went blank. I was confused about what happened. It had cut off while he was leading into his breakthrough. The turning point, it seemed, in his life. I asked myself, *How did he find the strength and confidence to overcome the things that he did?* Those questions I did not get answers to when needed. The TV went off when it could have been something I needed to hear—could have saved my life. I did all I could to get it back on. I played with the antenna to hopefully get a signal, but that was not it. I slapped both sides of the television, but it did nothing but bring attention. The librarian looked at me and said, "I turned it off. We are now closing." Little did she know, if I wanted to bad enough, I could have gotten that remote from her. But because of GM, I had my music to listen to.

I bopped my way around the neighborhood listening to my cassette player. A few blocks away from where I was staying was the Racine Liquor Store. Down the street from the liquor store in Englewood was an abandoned building I chose to stay at for the night. As I entered the building, there was a group of three teens posted on the staircase. I walked up the flight of stairs and then felt one of the teens grab me by the waist and press me against the wall. He demanded I give up my headphones, which I refused to do. His two other friends stood behind him and laughed. I told them, "I don't want any problems." They laughed again, and the situation turned hostile. One of the teens lifted his shirt to reveal the pistol he had, thinking it would scare me. Another friend came from behind and struck me in the mouth. As I fell to my side, I reached under my shirt, grabbing for my .38. As I reached under my shirt, the bigger teen grabbed my hand and felt for the .38. He pulled it from under my shirt and looked me in the eye, aimed, and pulled the trigger, shooting me in my left foot. The one who punched me snatched the headphones from around my neck and they all ran off.

I lay there in pain. My foot was on fire. It burned. I screamed out loud, begging for someone to come help. I was in the building alone until a lady came from behind, placed a blanket over me, and said, "Don't worry, my boy, help is on the way." At that point, I heard sirens, I saw the flashing lights reflecting in the dark. She then walked away but stood at the bottom of the stairway, waiting for the paramedics to arrive.

The paramedics kept asking me questions about what happened, where I lived, where my parents were. Questions I did not have answers to. I just tossed and turned, eventually getting strapped down to the gurney to hold me still. I lay there wondering if my mother and father had felt this pain, this burning-hot sensation. As we arrived at Cook County Hospital, it was like a scene out of a movie. I was being ushered into a room, witnessing all sorts of patients in need of care as I went by. Some had been shot, stabbed, beaten, burned. I heard babies crying and saw folks in the corner being aggressive with the police and drunks.

I was placed in an operating room to have the bullet removed from my foot. They put me under and once I woke up, nobody was there. One of the worst feelings I felt was waking up out of surgery, realizing no one was at my bedside. Once again, I was alone. Seconds later, a young nurse named Amina came into the room and asked me, "How are you holding up?" She could tell I was not all the way right, but she gave me comfort. She told me she knew my Uncle Earl and he was on his way to come pick me up.

I gave her a crooked smile. I said, "You know my uncle?"

She said, "Yes, I do. We are good friends. I told him I would look after you until he arrived."

She did just that. She waited, stayed there, even when police came in and tried to question me. She told them she was a friend of the family and that my uncle was on the way. She knew if they could not get ahold of my parents then I could have become a ward of the state. My uncle finally walked in. He came in and grabbed my hand, asking me if everything was okay and saying I would be going home with him. The officers asked to speak with my uncle, and they then left the room. My uncle came back in, followed by Amina. She had the discharge paperwork. I was set to go home with my uncle.

Fourteen days living on the streets, and no one had bothered me until that night. That night set me on a new path in my life. A path that was the way it was because of my upbringing. My life was a one-sided coin. I did not have a choice. That night allowed me to be in the care of a man who tried to steer me right, but I was never meant to do good. I knew the actions I had committed meant I was not normal like everyone else. Going home with my uncle directed me on the path of becoming the man my father once was. Then again, I would ask myself, if I grew up hating my father, would I still have become the man he was? But none of that matters. Life was the way that life was.

Psalm 31:10–14: "For my life is spent with grief, and my years with sighing: my strength faileth because of mine iniquity, and my bones are consumed. I was a reproach among all mine enemies, but especially among my neighbors, and a fear to mine acquaintance: they that did see me without fled from me. I am forgotten as a dead man out of mind: I am like a broken vessel. For I have heard the slander of many: fear *was* on every side: while they took counsel together against me, they devised to take away my life. But I trusted in thee, O Lord: I said, Thou *art* my God."

CHAPTER FIVE

One-Sided Coin

Throughout our drive home, I kept silent. Too afraid to speak. Too afraid to tell my uncle I had watched the carnage of my daddy's death, the execution of my mother was done by me—but what lay heavy on me was telling my uncle I was molested by three men my mother knew as she lay across from me with another woman. The more he asked, the more frightened I became. He knew something was not right. He never once yelled or raised his voice. He spoke softly, relaxed. The way he conducted himself was terrifying. I cried in the passenger seat of my uncle's car. Crocodile tears, I once heard my mother say. Pulling into an alleyway, my uncle stopped the car and told me to get out as he got out. We met at the nose of his truck. He bent down to my level and looked me in the eyes and, with no stutter in his voice, he asked, "What happened?" I told him I killed Ma. I told him she did not love me anymore. She did not love Dad anymore, so she had killed him as I stood there and watched. My uncle's eyes became watery as he felt the pain in my voice.

My uncle had never raised a child before. For one given reason, my uncle knew having attachments would have made him weak. But because I was the only son to his brother, he kept me around and molded me into the man that he was, that my father was. He told me stories about their upbringing, how they were raised by Lil Stace. The murders, robberies, kidnapping, the pain they caused to the families of their victims.

I told my uncle that my mother's body had been left at the house. That night, we drove to my mother's home. It was my uncle, his friend, and myself. My uncle told me to wait in the car as the two of them went inside. I waited and waited, and moments later, I saw an orange glare in the living room window, followed by another orange glare reflecting on the neighbor's house from my parents' room. My uncle and his friend ran out of the house with a duffle bag they had collected from the home. As they entered the truck, I sat in the back seat and watched the fire burn down anything and everything that was in the house, including the lifeless body of my mother. After that day, we never once talked about that moment. My uncle told me it was handled and that was it. We were informed by the police what happened, and that was when my uncle took full custody of me.

The first few years of living with my uncle were about lessons, being able to be a man of understanding, wits, developing patience. He knew I carried the ability to kill; that was easy. He wanted to know for sure that I knew how to survive. To be able to see things for what they really were. I read books; I was homeschooled. He tried to get me enrolled at a Chicago public school, but I just could not fit in. On the first day of fifth grade, I came across a white boy who had a troubled mouth. It was during an after-school program where this kid said my mother was a stripper. Honestly, I did not know what a stripper was, but the way he said it was aggressive. I felt he wanted to hurt me. I acted on what I knew. I tried to hurt him. I did not want to just punch him, I wanted to kill him. I was not going to stop until someone broke it up.

I picked up a jump rope I saw on the floor. I originally swung a fist at him, and as he backed up, he turned his back to me. That was when I picked up the rope. Before he could catch it, the rope was wrapped around his neck. I tied the loose ends to the palm of my hands and pulled. He could not break free. As I kept pulling, his body became weaker. He should have gone to reach for my eyes, but instead he tried to get his finger under the rope. The program leader ran in and separated us. She asked, "What happened?" The room was silent. He tried to speak, but it seemed as if he had doubled tongues. He could not get a coherent word out his mouth. The teacher had never encountered an experience like this before. I eventually told her why I did what I did. I told her he was a problem. He talked nasty to me. She never saw a kid like me, she said.

"What is wrong with you?" she asked me.

I told her, "I would do the same thing to you that I did to him, so watch your mouth."

She was speechless. Fearful for her life, she sat there and cried in front of me. She had no reason to cry but she did. Said that I was evil and that my uncle was coming to pick me up.

After this incident, my uncle introduced me to a woman name Ree Bee K. She was my mentor/teacher. She and my uncle had a relationship, but they never considered themselves to be in a relationship. My uncle did not want attachments, nor did Ree Bee K. want to be with him. She knew who he was and what he was about. One thing about Ree Bee K. was she had her own children but loved me as if I were her own. She knew my struggles but never once gave up on me. She dedicated her time to my self-development. You do not discover who you are; you decide who you are and focus on that. She wanted me to be a better man than my uncle was. She believed in me. But if it were not for my uncle, I would have never met her.

As I grew older, from ages nine through thirteen, my uncle had me in the garden. Every morning, we would go water the flowers that we planted. We did a lot of garden work, dug holes, planted new soil, and then turned over the dirt, placed the seeds, pulled weeds, built the foundation for a flower bed, and mowed the lawn. We did it all. I enjoyed gardening. The purpose of that lesson was to help develop patience with people, places, and things.

Every Sunday, we would go to my uncle's farmhouse in Streator. My uncle had horses and chickens on his farm. There was one horse he had named Lady of Choice. She was a beauty. Her coat was a mix of black and gray. She was named after my grandma's favorite horse. One of the exercises we did every time we went to the farmhouse was to catch a chicken. His way of life was that if you could not catch a chicken, you did not eat. Meaning if you did not work, you did not make money. We would spend hours running around in circles trying to catch a chicken. He had an electric wand he used to get the chickens excited, and as soon as they went off, you did too. The first couple of times, he would allow me to use both of my hands to catch the chicken, but as I became better, I would be drawn to only one hand, which became harder but I became more efficient. My agility was solid, I could move more quickly, but he wanted to try my senses, which took time. But we got there.

He would put me and the chicken in a large, fenced cage, blindfolded, with minutes on the clock to catch the chicken. I would have to listen for sounds, noises, energy, all of which enhance the hearing and the senses. The first hundred times, I would fall on my face, but eventually, when I caught my first chicken blindfolded, that became our dinner that night. It was an accomplishment meal. While the chicken cooked, my uncle and I would sit alongside the pond behind his house and feed the ducks. We would take moldy, rotten bread and break it down into pieces so we could feed the ducks. He would say, "When life gives you crumbs, make a meal out of it." It was funny, yet so true, and it was his way of escaping. It was refreshing. For myself, it became very therapeutic. My uncle was never apologetic for anything he had ever done; it was all based on survival, what he knew. That was what he wanted me to know and understand, and that is why I was raised the way I was. He could not teach me what he did not know.

For my fourteenth birthday, my uncle hosted a party for me and some of his brothers from the Legion of Doom. There was a rat amongst that group. Before everyone showed up, my uncle told me who the rat was and what he looked like. My uncle said, "Gain their power by playing to their fantasy." In other words, know his weakness, which was the drink. He was a drunk.

Once the party got going, everyone was having an enjoyable time, it seemed. It was my uncle, three other men, and myself. My uncle sent me to the kitchen to gather drinks, but it was more than just drinks. He wanted me to kill a man—the rat. A lot was at stake for me and my uncle. I was tasked to kill a man, and if I failed, then it would make my uncle look bad. They could have killed us over it. Have us on our knees with a pistol aimed at our mouths. It was either him or us. I had no relationship with this man, so there were no feelings, emotions, attached. Music in the background canceled out the noise of me smashing a few lightbulbs on the kitchen countertop. Using a rolling pin allowed me to crush the glass into very fine pieces that were still sharp enough to cut the inside of his throat. Mixed with a few crushed ice cubes, he would never be able to tell. But my nerves started to get the better of me. If I were to have walked out at that moment, he would have questioned why I seemed on edge, shaky. Sweat dripped off my forehead into his drink. The room began to feel hot. I needed to figure how to cure this feeling. I opened the freezer to grab more ice, and I placed it in a large bowl to rest my hand in until it turned numb. I was seeking that sleepy-foot feeling you get when you sit on the toilet for too long. My hand became cold and wet and it had no feeling. It felt swollen, and that was when I knew I was ready.

I walked into the living room where they were playing poker. I handed everyone their drinks. To not make him suspicious of my doings, I walked over and sat on the sofa.

I looked over in his direction and I watched this piss-poor excuse of a man drink every drop I poured, swallow every ice cube that was crushed. His death was like a fish that did not get enough water. Slow and painful. A crooked smile grew on my face as I watched him take his first cough, followed by another and the itching and scratching of his neck.

Every time he talked or swallowed, the sharp edges of the glass would cut the inside of his throat. Blood spat out his mouth, pain and anger in his eyes. This was the first time I had witnessed a man coughing up his own blood. He rose to his feet, pacing in my direction as I stood there watching a man dying slowly. His body collapsed to the floor and he gargled on his own blood, his fingers tearing the skin around his neck, hoping it would simmer the torture he felt as he died at my feet. The brothers at the table not only liked me but enjoyed me because I was creative with violence; they idolized my drive, my ambition. They welcomed me with open arms to the brotherhood under my uncle's care.

We celebrated with drinks and laughter as a dead body lay on the floor across from us. As night fell, everyone left. My uncle told me to hang tight; he had to step out and would be right back. This was when I found out just how these men covered their tracks. How they did not get caught. How bodies were never discovered. About an hour later, my uncle returned in a black hearse with Legions Crematorium, LLC, written on the side. Once in the house, my uncle and his partner began to gather any trace that could put them at fault. The body lay on a rug my uncle had put down. They rolled his body in the rug and zipped it inside a body bag that they carried out. We drove about an hour away with the dead body in the back of the vehicle. These brothers owned a crematorium business that would allow them to cremate the bodies as if nothing had ever happened. They would just vanish. Disappear. No trace. Those men who dealt with my uncle, they respected him. They honored him. He never half-stepped anything he ever did. My uncle said, "If you honor where you are with your best effort, it will lead to it. To the thing that you want to become. As you walk along, you will stumble into it." Well, I stumbled!

I did my first bid at the age of fifteen for possession of a firearm. Later, I found out it was a setup by my uncle to see if I would snitch on him for giving me the gun, but it was also a training method to prepare me to withstand the conditions of being locked up or adapting quickly to the environment you are in. Having your freedom stripped away from you. Everything that was once comfortable, well, that no longer exists. All your senses become sharper. You become more observant. Reconditioning your mind so you do not break down and kill yourself. I watched a man hang himself in front of me. He asked for my help, saying if I did not get the officers, then he would do it. I told him I could not. So, he did it. Tied one end of a sheet around his neck and the other end to the rail in the shower cell and allowed his body to stoop down as he began to choke. An inmate came from around the corner and called for the officer to come help. If it was his plan to kill himself and I came between that, then that would have made it my problem. And if you take on a problem, be willing to die for it.

While being processed at intake, I stood in line in front of a kid, a white boy around my age. His body went into shock and he started having a seizure. I felt a hit on the back of my arm, causing me to turn around and see him leaning backward, falling toward the ground. A loud boom sounded as his head hit the floor. White foam poured out of his mouth. The ERTs turned him on his side so he would not bite down on his tongue. I was out of my element.

For the first week, I did not eat or shower. I spoke with my uncle on the phone and he said there was nothing he could do; I would have to sit and do my time. As we were getting ready to end the call, his voice began to crackle. I did not think much of it, but he said, "Regardless of the amount of time you have, you never really know who you will see on the other side of the gate. I love you, and keep your head up." And that is when he ended the call. At that moment, I knew I had to adapt to my environment. I quickly adjusted, but I cried my first night in general population. An older kid named Can't Get Right came to me and told me to not do that shit here. Told me to go wipe my face off with cold water and come back to sit down. He taught me the rules of the world. He mentioned for me to move around, told me I should put in a request to work, sign up for laundry detail. It worked out for me. I was able to meet folks I would have never met.

While working in the unit, I met a kid who had been in there much longer than I had but was getting ready to be transferred to an adult facility for his crime. He showed me

Darren S. Hardaway Jr.

how to make money, how to survive, how to eat. He showed me how to sell clothes in exchange for commissary food. Each day we would go to the unit and exchange dirty clothes for cleaner clothing. As they came down to get their clothing, they would tell me what they wanted. I would then give the newest items, such as state babies, shower shoes, underwear, thermals, socks, pants, and tops. Whatever I could provide, I would sell. As they went back up to their cell, they would gather their commissary food, mix it up with their dirty clothes, walk back down, and throw it in the bin. Once we got back to the laundry room, I would collect. I made about thirty dollars a day selling clothes. At the end of the night, I had a guy who would put together a large pizza-size burrito that we would place in the oven. I had some homies who worked kitchen detail and they would bring chorizo and anything that could be added. So, every night, everyone in the dorm would eat. I had it going for about a month until the night these two guys wanted to jump someone I knew in the unit. My guy could have held his own—he was built for it—but I would have felt wrong if I allowed that to happen. As they stood on their feet, they called him out and told him to come to the back. My homie got out of bed and rose to his feet. I got up as well. My homie, Jorge, got out of his bunk, but since Jorge came on my behalf, all the other Mexicans who respected Jorge came to my aid too. But nothing happened. That night everybody slept in their own bunk.

The following day, a few ERT's—Emergency Response Team—came over to my bunk and tossed my stuff around. One of those two boys ratted me out to the COs—the correctional officers. They told the CO I was selling clothing and that they should check my bins. I had three bins, two with food and the other with clothing and reading material. They discovered I had illegal contraband and extra clothing. I ended up doing two weeks in solitary confinement; some call it "the hole."

There was an older kid I met in the hole who was in there for a double homicide. He had killed a couple while under the influence of drugs. One of the things my uncle used to tell me: Never do drugs or drink alcohol. Be present in the moment. Some guys kill while under the influence of drugs or liquor to mask the moral dilemma they face because they know it is wrong. This kid I met, he was on the brink of doing a life sentence, just waiting to be transferred. We started talking, engaging in conversation. He asked me if I would be down to join his gang, talked about how "I'mma need it if I'mma be in here."

I told him politely, "I'm good," and where I was from. He honored that. Asked me about some cats I knew around my area who were out robbing elderly women. I told him, "Yeah, I heard about it."

He looked at me directly and said, "When I see them, I'm going to kill them." I nodded my head as we then engaged in further conversation.

I was released from the hole and sent to B-Pod, which they called "gladiator dorm." My first day out of the hole, I went to my cell and found I had a roommate, an older kid waiting to be transferred to Stateville for armed robbery with attempted murder. We started working out, he gave me a few books to read, we played card games like casino, and he blessed me with some food to hold me over. Later that afternoon, we went down for chow. Single-file line, waiting to gather our trays. I was next in line. I saw I had a brownie on my tray. As I walked up, this inmate came from behind me and took my tray and walked off. He took my food. My brownie. I did nothing about it. We all went back to our cell, ate our food, went back down to return our trays, and returned to our cells. I had been mistreated in front of everyone. My roommate said, "Everyone now is going look at you as weak, prey. What happened is you just let another man steal your meal. You have to own your shit."

I felt cornered like a wild animal that had become unstable. What I did next must be felt throughout the entire jail from all wings. To have ultimate victory, you must be ruthless. Every effort deserves a reward. I started to understand the rules of the world I was living in. Lions and lambs—the hunter and the hunted. It is easier to cope with a bad conscience than live with a bad reputation. Jeremiah 10:14, "Every man is brutish in his own knowledge."

Every door opened so we could go out for recreational time. Everyone was sitting in their groups, talking about mostly nothing. My cellmate was sitting amongst his peers. I waited for my moment. There was no force bigger than a concentrated focus. I watched as the inmate walked up to his cell and closed his door slightly. He covered his door window with wet toilet paper so no one could see inside. I allowed a moment to go by and then walked up to his cell, popped open his door, caught him with his pants down, dick in his hand, jerking off. I rushed into his room. He rose to his feet, pants down to his ankles. I slammed his face against the concrete wall and blood gushed out his mouth.

Forearm pressed to his neck, I shoved my fist repeatedly into his back, bruising his kidney. A stream of bloody piss oozed down his leg. He let out dog cries, pleading for help as loud as he could as he felt the discomfort of my knuckles thrashing into his back. My feet were covered in his bloody piss. The voices of the ERTs entered the dorm, but I did not let up. I wanted this boy to feel what I had felt: humiliation. I pressed my body up against his and he felt my cock in between the crack of his ass. He had long, girlish hair with a shampoo scent, colored eyes, fair complexion, very passable. When you are pushing inside of a person, you can close your eye and use your imagination. I told him he was cute as I gently licked his earlobe, grabbing his soft bare ass with the palm of my hand. My intentions were never done for intimacy; I had an animalistic nature inside me that had a desire that needed to be filled. The same thing I felt when I stood in the bathroom looking at myself in the mirror, before stepping to my mother when I was only a child. It's a comparable itch that needs to be scratched, similar to a man, or woman, who is lustful, of having strong feelings of a sexual thirst. That was the itch I needed to scratch.

The ERTs sprinted into the room, tackling me down onto his bunk as his body collapsed. I wanted to smile but I could not. I wanted to laugh but I could not. I wanted to find some level of emotion inside of me that would allow me to feel, but there was nothing but coldness. I watched as he fell into a slump, lying in his own urine. He could no longer stand on his own feet. Blood dripped down between his legs. Only we knew the truth, but chatter went around that he had been beaten and raped. Escorted out of his cell, I looked over at my cellmate and he smiled and nodded his head. I was yet again sent to the hole to finish out the remaining ten months of my sentence.

That night, I fantasized about what it would have been like if that moment had played out. If the ERTs had never come. My train of thought was broken when my homie next door banged on my wall. He was sent to the hole for fighting. His roommate had left a chocolate candy bar on his bunk while he was out in the rec area. I asked him what that meant. He said, "It's a rite of passage. If I ate it, then he would have topped me. So, I fucked him up on general principle, and here I am." Sad thing about it was, a few weeks later, the same night upon his release, he was shot and killed outside a girl's house in Joliet. He was a good dude I called MB, a shortened version of his name.

I spent the remainder of my time in the hole working out, writing, and reading. I did not allow the walls to become my friend. If I had allowed myself to remain in my head, I would have committed suicide. But the books, exercising, and writing were what helped me get through. As the CO came to my cell door and told me, "Pack your shit, you're going home," I felt unease. I did not know what to feel. I knew what life was like here and what life was like on the outside. As the guard walked me out, he said, "Life is a full circle. Eventually your actions will catch up to you. You just do not know when, where, how, or why! Remember, that Slim."

CHAPTER SIX

Mirrored Image

Upon my release, a small gathering was held on my behalf. When I arrived, I was led into the back bedroom by a woman I did not have much interest in. They called her Kitty Kat. She was a dark-skinned woman with a petite frame. She was not one for small talk. Kitty Kat immediately started to strip herself down to her bare skin. She pushed my shoulders back until I was on my back across the bed. My pants were then unfastened and a hand gripped my shaft as she positioned my cock in her mouth. I could not find excitement, but I was stimulated. The slightest touch could have aroused me. I had never partaken in any sexual relationships with a woman before. She would be my first.

A level of embarrassment started to overpower my other emotions. I suddenly felt threatened and resorted to an act of aggression. My eyes were closed; voices of passion encircled my thoughts. I wanted to hurt this person and finish what I started in jail. I felt embarrassed because I started to visualize myself having a sexual encounter with that inmate. So I did what I did. As she climbed on top of me, I rolled her over, face down, mounted myself on top of her, and pressed her face into the mattress. My cock was already wet from her mouth. She yelled for help, but that only excited me. It started to remind me of the inmate as he cried out. I pushed the head of my aroused cock inside her anal cavity. The pain in her voice as she cried for help only made it worse. I licked her earlobe and softly uttered, "This ass is soft." I asked her, "How does Daddy's cock feel, nigga?" I told her, "Tell me you love me." I had no control over myself. I wanted to finish what I had been fantasizing about. Since I could not physically get to him, I closed my eyes and imagined it was him and not her.

My uncle ran into the room and threw me off her, but I was mentally gone. I jumped to my feet and charged at my uncle. Before I could get any closer to him, he swung, connecting his fist with my jaw. That brought me back to life. I sat there on the ground, not really understanding what had just happened. My uncle asked Kitty Kat what happened. She said, "He raped me. Fucked me in the ass and I did not want that. I told him to stop. He started calling me a nigga, talking about this and talking about that. He thought he was fucking a boy."

My uncle did not know how to understand nor process that information. He told Kitty Kat to go shower and clean herself off. As she went into the bathroom, my uncle came to me and told me, "Do not worry about it. Shit happens. I will fix it." He felt there was a chance that she could have exposed his nephew for being a homosexual or even disrespect my uncle's name by saying he was raising a homosexual. Either way, she had to go. She knew too much. My uncle grabbed a pillow and his pistol and went into the bathroom. The pillow was used to protect him from the blood splatter. After I heard the gun go off, he came back out and said, "It'll be all right. I love you, kid."

Later that night, I sat at the dinner table with my uncle. He never asked me what happened or why I acted that way, but he had a good sense that I was not all the way right mentally. I told him when I was nine, I was assaulted by three men in front of my mother. These men took turns on me. Using me, abusing me, to where I grew to think this was the normal way of sexual engagement. My first sexual act was with a man. Being with a woman, I did not know how to act. So I acted out in rage. I told him I did not want to do that again. He asked me, "What do you want to do in life?"

I replied, "I want to be like you and my father."

My uncle said, "Your father was good man—a good-hearted man—but his personality made him a very dangerous and violent man. You have the mechanics your father had; it is a generational curse. But all things I knew and know I have and will inculcate in your mind as long as you listen to what I teach. You are more ruthless and callous than your father was. He enjoyed the company of women, but you do not. Keep it that way, and no one can or will have leverage over you. No one can or will be able to reach you if you do not want to be reached. Understand me, no one knows the path I've traveled—the pain, the hurt, the violence that I endured to become this gentle— but a man of great wrath shall suffer punishment!"

I became a student to what he taught. He became impressed with the way I conducted myself over certain junctures. We would go into the woods at night. It would be us and a few of his brothers from the Legion of Doom. These men would tell me to put my hands behind my back and if I were to cry, they would hit me even harder, body-slam me into a tree, punch me in my chest. When I was asleep, they would wake me by putting out cigarettes on my arm—small wrinkle blisters would form—just so we could go jogging or study our literature. It was all about the craft. I became obedient and shadowed his tracks.

Before I was able to take my pledge, which I did in the end, my uncle had to vouch for me. Bring me forth to the brotherhood. My uncle and Brother Rivera introduced me to all the brothers around the room, and they sat me down so I could answer the questions that Brother McCullough had to ask. I had to show them I was worthy—a beast—and knew that if I were to betray the oath, I may have my throat cut from ear to ear, my tongue pulled out, and tossed into the Red Sea. These men of the Legion of Doom became my brothers.

When I was first introduced to Lil Stace, he was older, washed up, but he held his own. That is why he remained in his position for as long as he had. He was respected amongst men and had fighters who were ready to shake on his command. But being the head of a charter, to hold that throne, he had to be an active rider, still able to drive his motorcycle at his age.

Not long after, my uncle became ill. Diagnosed with lung cancer. He neglected the chemotherapy and any other treatment that was offered. My uncle was a warrior; he was not trying to prolong his life, nor was I going to force something on him that he did not want. That would have been selfish, and who was I to intervene with God's plan? So, I let it be. Allowed nature to do what nature does.

Every morning, we would eat a big breakfast together. He knew that was my thing. Breakfast was our way of bonding. As we ate, we would either watch *General Hospital* or we would just eat and talk. I would listen more than anything. Listen to his stories, the knowledge he gave, and I would apply it to myself. He advised me to go out and perform charity work, be of aid to brothers and sisters who came from a struggle and provide an outlet for betterment for their well-being. Some words I would never forget, like how he expressed the way he viewed me. He did not think of me as a fool; he respected me for who I was, but what he saw of me was not who I was. He saw a better version of me that was the opposite of who I was.

There were times when I had to step out from his company because I had an obligation to the organization I had to maintain. During one assignment, I came back and found my uncle facedown on the floor. He had been trying to warm some food in the microwave but did not have the strength to stand on his feet. No maid, no family, no friends, no one to be at his side, but they did not need to be because I should have been there. It reminded me of when I woke up in the hospital alone and no one was there. So, I hired an in-home nurse who stayed with him every day until he was no longer present. The night before his transition, I sat at his bedside, got down on my knees, and prayed. I asked, "Please take my uncle so he does not have to go through this pain and suffering. He is ready."

My uncle grabbed my hand and his last words to me were, "Let love lead you home."

The following morning was when he transitioned over.

I felt hopeless. My guardian, mentor, the person I loved, was gone. I thought God was selfish for leaving me alone yet again. Granted, I prayed for the calling, but I could not fathom the thoughts that circled my mind. Crying was not therapeutic for me at that time. I wanted to go to war with God. I wanted to make Him feel what I felt as we battled at the Jabbok River. My pain was enough that I could have set the sky on fire and the world would have felt it. But my desires were merely a wish.

After my uncle's passing, I began to drink whiskey to surpass my everyday thoughts. I did not know how to grieve; I did not know what grief was. I did not want to accept being alone again. I slept every night at his grave. I told him about how I developed a bloodthirsty urge to kill, but I had been taught not to make a permanent decision on a temporary problem. The amount of pain I bottled inside me would only result in a craving of self-annihilation. I went home the following morning and no one was there. The nurse who was looking after my uncle had not come around since his passing. The house was empty. Which I knew. I knew that the house was the safest place for me to be. There or beside his grave. Once home, I started spoiling myself with a bottle of whiskey. Halfway through the bottle, I found myself standing in the bathroom, holding a six-inch razorblade in my left hand. There was a glow that shined off my bald head as I was contemplating the idea of inflicting pain on myself to protect those around me.

There is no victory when there is no war. The fight was not with the outside, but it was with me—within. Standing with tears I had not seen in years, I was frail, but that is where I found my power. I sacrificed my physical appearance to give myself the upper hand I needed to regain my self-control. Piercing the skin, I drew the blade down my face from the corner of my eye down to my jawline. The blood from my face oozed down my wrist as the blade was pulled down. The whiskey numbed any pain I could have felt. I stood there in front of the mirror, looking at the man I had grown into. That moment did not only strengthen me, it made me. I grew to become more violent, dangerous, and self-disciplined. Nothing could have stopped my growth. Brain is stronger, mind is clearer, and will is firm. Adversity introduces a man to himself.

***

Once I became tapped back into the function of things, I reached out to Lil Stace for work. He met me at Satan's Abyss, a church that was the mother home of where we would conduct our meetings. Just he and I met. The church was located on Sixty-Ninth and Steward. It was a vacant building but the property was owned by Lil Stace. I was offered a job that accommodated what I was feeling inside. There was a bounty per head for a family and the associates of that family. My duty was to make this family extinct. Anyone who carried their last name—man, woman, or child. The orders came down and I accepted. For whatever reason, I was given the information of why this job was of importance. A brother from The Devil's Kings had received a sentence for a crime he had committed. This specific member sat at the left of Lil Stace during chapel. That made him the VP of the charter. The judge refused to do things the organization's way. The judge wanted it to be known that he could not be bought. The judge became cocky. He gave the maximum sentence. During the trial, the judge mentioned, "No one nor any organization, especially The Devil's Kings, can bully me into being in their favor." He made it known that his comment was directed to the brotherhood. Lil Stace took that taunt personally. The judge needed to be held accountable for the deaths that were to come. Lil Stace wanted him to live with that guilt. Knowing your family and friends are all dead because you chose to come for us. So that was the job.

A few days later, I drove out to San Diego, California. With the information provided, I started with the only son the judge had. This kid was easy. I spent nights outside his apartment, watching his every move. I followed him to work, to the restaurants he ate at, to the fitness gym, Bally's. I had him whenever I was ready. I do not believe I slept during my stay. My mind was trained to think that once I closed my eyes, I would lose the opportunity. He could just vanish without me knowing, or he could have the upper hand on me. Either way, sleep was not worth the risk. I pursued him as long as I did to know the type of people he was connected with. Watching him for those few days, I gained the whereabouts of his closest friends and the lady he had in his life. Because if I could not get to him, I could get to them. Having them in my possession would give me influence over him. It all works out the way it does.

I already knew which apartment he was in. His name was on the mailbox. I waited until midnight before I entered the building. As I approached his door, I heard chatter as if he had company. I was already committed; there was no turning back at this point. I knocked on his door and heard a woman, say, "Babe who is that? Did you order pizza?"

He responded, "I don't know. Let me see."

As he opened the door, I used my shoulder to forcefully enter his home. The force of my entry caused him to stumble backward, losing his balance. I grabbed him by the neck and threw him down on the floor. His girlfriend was screaming as loud as she could. Before I shot her, I shot him. I did not want him getting up, trying something stupid to protect her. As I shot him, she became immobilized, and the screaming stopped. She was in shock. She did not feel anything as the initial bullet penetrated her forehead, followed by the second bullet.

Soft cries from a baby came from the backroom. As I opened the door, the daughter of the parents I just murdered was staring at me. Her tiny hands were gripping the frame of her crib, holding herself up. My job was to kill them all. The deep, demonic voices echoed in my head, instructing me to do just that. I was hollowed at the core. Empty inside. I picked the baby up and laid her down. Her short arms reached for air. I reached over and grabbed a pillow off the mattress and placed it over the baby's head. The pillow blocked my eyesight so I would not see the baby's face. The barrel of the .357 pressed down to the pillow. I stood there for a second, but it felt longer. I released my grip from around the trigger and picked up the pillow. I locked eyes with Annamae, the baby's name. Annamae, which means "God has favored me" in Hebrew. I found out what her name was because she was wearing a name charm necklace.

I left her lying there as I went into the bathroom. I stared at my image in the mirror, a tear forming in the corner of my eye and eventually rolling down my cheek. I realized at that moment, this was me becoming my father. I stood in the bathroom and cried. I had gone down a path of uncharted territory I had never experienced before. A spiritual war between good and evil. A vision of God and Satan on each shoulder, tugging away at my soul. The hands of the unknown reaching out of the fire, begging to be saved. Their voices screamed louder than baby Annamae. I cupped my hands under the sink faucet as the water overflowed. I dipped my head into my hands. Clearing my thoughts, I heard a powerful voice I recognized to be my father's, saying, "Show yourself a man." At that moment, I stood firm in the shoes of my father. But what made me a man was to not make the same mistakes my father made.

I overheard the sound of the television from the living room and the cries from Annamae. The voices that came from the stereo sounded familiar. The background music was noise I had heard before. It overpowered the cries of Annamae. And there it was, the K. Wynn talk show. I walked out of the bathroom and looked over at Annamae. I knew her cries would not stop, so I held her in my arms, and I became gentle with her. We inched closer to the television in the living room. Darren Hardaway and K. Wynn showed themselves on the screen. The part that had cut off when I was a child is where the program began.

Darren was talking about going to prison. God will use an enemy to get you to your destiny. Prison was Darren's enemy. Darren talked about how he was introduced to a woman named Charee once he came home. She was a pivotal figure in his life. She became his mentor. She helped him see things in himself that he did not see. Look at a man in the way that he is, he becomes worse, but look at a man in the way he could be, and he becomes better. God sent her to help Darren realize that he is the vehicle to his full potential, to becoming the man he wants to be. Not just a better man, but a worthy servant to God. She became his financial investor in his first endeavor. She used her own money with the help of her friends to kick-start his first business. Hardaway Custom Hats & Apparel (HCHA), a T-shirt-printing company he started in his mother's basement. As his company grew, he became known worldwide. He not only was producing orders in the States, but organizations from overseas in Afghanistan were reaching out as well. The freemasons established the bridgework for that to happen.

At the end of his first year, HCHA had an extensive résumé of Fortune 100 companies, organizations, and individuals who hired Darren for his services. Darren knew nothing about printing, designing, or business. He prided himself on his work ethic. If he knew nothing at all, he at least knew how to work and was not afraid to take a risk. During the growth of his company, he enrolled himself in a community college with the GED he obtained while incarcerated at Dixon Springs Boot Camp. He studied marketing, and in class was where he met a fellow classmate, Mr.

Parker, who was the father to a woman named Milon. Mr. Parker made the introduction. The relationship between Milon and Darren was indescribable, he would say. The bond, the love they had for each other, was unconditional, but they had their moments. The relationship started off by Milon wanting Darren to print her shirts, but she also saw that he was a big guy, so she offered him a job to work security for her movie premiere, *The Lies We Tell but the Secrets We Keep, Part Three*. During that event, Darren became inspired by her. He saw how she took a blank piece of canvas and made art. She was an independent filmmaker, a talented one at that. I once heard Ermias "Nipsey Hussle" Asghedom say, "The highest human act is to inspire."

Later that night, after the event, Darren went home and started writing his first full-length feature film script, titled *What's It Worth*. The film focused on the idea of how if God gave up his only son for the people he loves, why can man not give up his life for the woman he loves? That is a question one may ask themselves. Everything you are doing, the relationship you are in, the job you hold, the decisions you make, what's it worth? Darren wanted to get a better understanding of film, so he got involved in acting. While working on the set of *Chicago PD*, Darren met a gentleman named Barry M. Barry was giving Darren a ride to the train station, because his license had been suspended. Public transportation was how Darren got around. During that ride, they had a conversation, and that conversation led Barry to become a co-producer who financially invested in the short film Darren wrote called *Hardcase*. Barry told him, "If you can write a good script, I will co-fund it." Barry did just that. Darren sent him the script in twenty-four hours and Barry signed off on it. But Darren's story got even richer as I listened.

Once you envision where you are going, you can then tell what you do not need, which means what are you willing to leave behind to get there? Shortly after *Hardcase* was produced, Darren left everything behind and relocated to Southern California to stay with the family of his brother at the time, JP. He told himself all he needed was two months and he would be able to make everything happen. He did exactly that. Darren got employed by a moving company called Omega Moving & Storage, saved his coins, and two months later, JP and he had a two-bedroom apartment of their own. Two-bedroom apartment, full-time job, a lady friend who bought him peanut butter when they first met at Vons, a member of a church home, Bayview Baptist, and a student at Southwestern Community College for film. Talk about growth—change. Run toward your destiny and you will distance yourself from your past.

Darren kept pursuing the reasons that brought him out there. He wanted to do better than he did while living in Chicago. He wanted growth. He kept making his movies, but he said after his last short film, *Psalm 23*, he needed more. Darren felt that he accomplished all he wanted in San Diego, but he no longer felt any growth. So, he put together a plan and chose to become homeless, to pursue an idea—a goal, a dream, a vision. Limits and boundaries do not play a part when you wear the crown. Conduct yourself like a king. Overcome self-imposed doubt. Know that you can get it done. Be confident in the path you choose. Darren chose to live out of the back seat of his SUV to make it happen, God willing, and he did.

During his travels, Darren was able to accomplish all he wanted. He got signed with a credible agency in Beverly Hills that was getting him auditions, and he was trained by an acting coach in Hollywood who could help him break down a thousand faces of a character, learn about living in the moment, and having a backstory for his character. Darren's acting coach was Anthony Gilardi. The home of the Anthony Gilardi Acting Studio in Hollywood was where Darren was able to study the craft. He did all this within two months. He had a plan and he followed through with it. Things were moving, moving fast. He accomplished more within that brief period than someone who spent a decade trying to do what he did. But we all move at our pace. The unfortunate thing was yet to come.

For side work, Darren worked for a moving company to make extra money. Out in Vegas, with his coworker Jerry, during the move, Darren was attempting to move a gun safe. Pulling and pushing the dolly toward him, he slipped. Trying to avoid the safe coming down on his leg, he rolled onto his left foot. In doing so, he fractured the bone that connects the big toe and the toe next to it. Once the fracture happened, the bone structure shifted to the left. In a warrior's state of mind, he tried to get back up and work but instantly fell on his face. During the interview, he mentioned how he took his shoe and sock off and found that his foot was swollen with two large baseball-sized lumps. During the drive back to Huntington Beach, California, Jerry and Darren joked about what had happened. They found humor in Darren's mishap and it only strengthened the relationship between the two. Jerry kept it to where Darren was living in the moment and not allowing him to be consumed by his thoughts. Watching the interview, I picked up the sense that Darren had a lot of love and respect for Jerry. Darren was scheduled to move a customer from California to Maryland, but he took a pay cut just so Jerry could be a part of that delivery. Jerry brought him around his hood in LA and introduced him to his family, allowed him to meet his grandfather, who had the working tools of a man. There is different level of love and respect you have for someone who leads you to their elders. Darren and Jerry were brothers in arms when it came to their work.

Now, homeless and disabled, Darren was unable to fully walk on his feet for nine out of the fourteen months he was living in his car. His family did not know about his struggle. He did it on his own. He chose that. He knew he could not go back home because it would have been the easy route. Taking an easy way out of a real situation is not what men do. He accepted all that came his way with the choice he made. The power of believing in oneself and having faith is what allowed him to rise above it all. Faith, focus, forward.

Now, it was time for Darren to have surgery on his foot. During the surgery, the surgeon made three surgical incisions, one on the top of his foot, the second on the side of his foot, and the third on his left leg. Darren refused to let the surgeon put an artificial bone in his foot. Offered the option, Darren told the surgeon he would rather have a piece of his bone taken from his leg to be applied to the foot. The surgeon proceeded with Darren's request. A piece of his bone from his leg was taken, but over the course of time it healed on its own.

After he had surgery, the intended person to pick him up never showed. He woke up in a room, alone, with no one there. Darren mentioned how while watching the film *Get Rich or Die Tryin'*, there was a scene where Curtis Jackson had surgery after being shot. After surgery, Curtis Jackson opened his eyes and saw his closest friends standing at his bedside. Darren mentioned when he saw that scene and it brought tears to his eyes. Because no one came for him. The nurse would not allow him to leave on his own for safety reasons. So, he called people he knew, including JP. Unfortunately, JP told him no, he could not stay with him. They did everything together under the sun. They were family and still are, but not everyone can continue your journey with you. You had fun with them, created memories, and had lessons, but that is as far as they can go. JP had his reasons why he said no, but they were based on a lack of understanding. Darren did what he did to further himself, but he never turned his back on his brother. He told JP to come with him to LA, that they could make it happen together, but JP was not for it. Knowing that, Darren made sure his apartment responsibilities did not fall at the feet of JP, but they did. He added that cable got cut off, but he fulfilled his promise. He sent money to JP to cover any expenses and paid off any debt owed to him or his brother.

One of the things JP had said to Darren was that he wanted to talk with him before he left, because he felt he probably would never see or talk to Darren again. Darren was not sure why he said that, but he spoke that into existence. I could tell Darren had missed the company of his brother and that love for him was still there. Darren made other phone calls, but either no one picked up or they said no. But those calls did not matter. When Darren needed JP the most, when nothing in the world should have mattered but the care for your friend, your brother, JP was not there for him.

When they cast you out, God will take you in. The pain, the tears, the hurt Darren felt were what relieved his mind of any medication he was given. He became fully conscious of his situation and his surroundings. He watched as a young girl awoke from her sleep, talking silly because of the medication she was given, but she had her mother at her side. Darren's nurse went to her supervisor and she told him what was happening. The supervisor came down and he and Darren had a conversation. He felt Darren was fully present and in the moment. The nurse ushered Darren outside in a wheelchair and they waited until the taxi arrived to take Darren to a motel where he had a room rented for a week. The hospital covered the taxi charge even though hospitals are not supposed to do that, because if anything goes wrong in transit, they can be held accountable. Nurses came to stay with Darren for a few days to make sure he was doing all right.

The week at the motel went by and, on the last day, Darren needed a place to finish his recovery stages. No family, no friends, no money, all he could do was pray. Praying led him in the direction of reaching out to the brothers and sisters of AGAS, the Anthony Gilardi Acting Studio group. A woman he barely knew responded to his post. Her name was Aerial W. However, Darren needed a way to get to Aerial because he was unable to drive himself due to the pain medication. A gentleman named Wes H., who once played in Darren's short film *Chat*, answered Darren's call and he came to his aid. Wes drove down to Huntington Beach from LA to pick Darren up, just to drive him to Aerial's home. She provided him the shelter he needed for his recovery, but he felt like more of an inconvenience by taking up her couch space. During his stay, he allowed her access to his SUV for her travels back and forth to work and to Vegas. He covered the dinner meals they shared together and left her some coins for his stay. He was thankful for her, but as soon as the cast came off his foot, he decided to go back to the struggle. Back to the SUV. During that time, he spent hours at the gym, hours at the library. He did what I did. But saying all that he said, he never once questioned God, but he said he "was more at peace within than the average person who had a roof over his head." And now Darren is doing everything he said he wanted to do. Robert Greene co-wrote a book with Curtis Jackson called, *The 50th Law*. In this body of work, Robert Greene says, "With energy and high morale, a human can overcome almost any obstacle and create opportunity out of nothing." Darren was proof of that testament. So, to me, he was successful.

Mr. K. Wynn, taken aback by Darren's story, went and said, "That's why I would reference you as Job. Such a powerful story of one's life. Having everything going for himself, then losing it all but keeping his faith and gaining everything he ever wanted and then some." Mr. K. Wynn asked, "But how? How did you manage to stay so strong, so positive through all that you went through?"

"No good man travels alone," Darren said. "I knew what I was going through was only temporary, and I would not allow myself to think it was a forever moment. I surrendered myself to God as opposed to a moment. I strengthened my faith. Philippians 4:13, 'I can do all things through Christ which strengtheneth me,' is what I recited habitually and reminded myself day to day of the reason why. Understanding the motive of the why is what permitted me to walk out of the fire with my hands up because I did not give in when the going became tough. Tough times don't last but tough people do! There is beauty in the ashes.

"I am not afraid to risk it all. Even if it did not go as planned, there is a lesson when you do not give up. It teaches you how to do better moving forward. Restrategize, replan, recreate, but never lose sight of what you want out of life or where you are headed! I have overcome life's obstacles. I am a world survivor. I am an overcomer and because of that, I am proud of the man that I am. I can die knowing I made my own way!"

Background music played as the show came to end. I looked down at Annamae as her soft touch caressed the side of my cheek. I closed my eyes to her touch. I finally felt an emotion. Something I had not felt in years. But here I was, remorseful. I felt guilty knowing what I had done. I was the Death that robbed her parents of their lives. There was nothing I could have done to make it right by her. But if there was something I could do, it would be to change my ways, like Darren. Annamae was my breakthrough. I became inspired. Seeing how Darren used his experiences to be the tools in his life to become the man he was destined to be. How he created his own way out nothing. How when it all went sideways, he turned to God, not man. How he was forgiven for his past doings. He kept chipping away at his imperfections; he set out seeking growth in his life. He strived to become a better man. A worthy servant to God. By doing so, it provided meaning and purpose in his life. He can say, with conviction, that he has made it.

CHAPTER SEVEN

Remission

There is a moment each day that Satan cannot find. Once you find that moment, make it last a lifetime. I discovered myself that night when I held baby Annamae in my arms. After that moment, I chose to walk a different path, embark on a journey on a road I had never voyaged beforehand. I wanted to do right, I wanted to do better than I did yesterday, but not as good as I would do tomorrow. I wanted growth in my life. My uncle once said, "Closest to the pain is closest to the power." I allowed myself to be guided by my heart and not my personality. I delivered baby Annamae to the doorstep of a church I knew of in San Diego. They were having Bible study on Wednesday nights at Bayview Baptist Church. I never attended service, but Darren, during his interview, had spoken highly of that church. There is a good brother named Brother Grubbs who works at the church. As I sat baby Annamae on the stoop, I banged on the door to get someone's attention. I then walked back around the corner to my car and waited until someone came out. When they did, they looked around and, as expected, they took baby Annamae in.

I drove back to Chicago that night. Took a little over a day to get back. I slept at rest areas and ate finger food. I did not want to allow myself to be consumed in public with the thoughts that would form in idle time. Social anxiety is a disease, and when filled, it can result in unwarranted behavior. I knew I was still battling a struggle within, and to be around people would have hurt me. Knowing is one thing but being is another, and I knew myself.

When I arrived back home, I immediately went to the grave site of my uncle and I just lay there on top of him. I expressed the details of my assignment and how the encounter with baby Annamae changed my life. Unpacking the elements of myself—my life—gave me clarity. It was a form of remission of my transgressions. It changed my attitude to see the opportunity, the blessing to do things differently. Bishop T. D. Jakes once said, "Never realizing who God anointed the most he always crushes severely." I lay on top of my uncle's burial site, broken and empty. Rain clouds began to form above me. A homeless woman came from the distance and advanced in my direction; no words were spoken. She looked at me and gave me a blanket. Her only words spoken were, "Peace in the path, my boy," as she then walked off pushing her cart. Her spirit was welcoming. The gifts she gave me provided comfort as I lay there till sunrise. It was a wealth of peace that I felt. This time, I could get some rest.

***

I awoke to crust on the corner of my mouth from drool. The sky had formed an angel-like cloud with the sun above the head. I could hear the laborer mowing the lawn. The air smelled different as I woke up with a smile on my face, holding on to those simple moments. I knew to believe is to live.

Gathering my belongings, I noticed a comrade who slept right outside the cemetery with nothing to cover himself and a missing left shoe. I call him a comrade because we were brothers in the same struggle. His arms were pulled inside his shirt; he was cold. I handed him the same blanket that was handed to me and gave him my shoe. Taking off my left shoe not only allowed me to be of service to him so he no longer had to travel barefoot, but it was sign to me of a new direction and life path. I told him if I had more, I would do more. He was appreciative of the little I was able to give. He was much older and wiser. He was wise as heaven is wide. As he rose to his feet, he asked me my name. Asked me if I had a son and told me when I do, I should get my son into baseball. We engaged in conversation as I stood there, and I told him my story. He told me to say history out loud. As I said it, I spoke the words, "His Story." He taught me how to see into words for what they really are. Like Darren's last name, "Hardaway": hard, but there is a way.

When he listened to what I had to say, his eyes grew wider as he spoke to me: "You are a prophet. You have angels watching over you. Somebody has been praying for you." I became emotional; I got light-headed. I kneeled down to one knee to collect myself. He told me he was on his way to the mountains; he had been traveling in the wilderness for some time now and now he wanted to take some time to focus on his plan. Told me to go down to the water and give an ear or an eye when looking for direction, because it would show itself to me. Left me with the words, "If no one has told you today, I will be the first to tell you that I love you." He gathered his belongings and traveled his way to the mountains.

I started on my way over to King Solomon's Temple. It was a place of refuge to seek wise counsel from Pastor C. L. Pitts Jr. Everything with man was built from the ground floor of King Solomon's Temple. It was how we constructed ourselves. Making good men better. Using the gavel to chip off our imperfections as we humbled ourselves on our square. My uncle would visit Pastor Pitts often, seeking guidance, asking for advice and to participate in charity work. Pastor Pitts knew of the lifestyle we lived, but he never cast judgment because he had his own stones to turn over before being the man he had grown to become. He believed in the saying "Love thy neighbor as you love thyself." Pastor Pitts was one of the very few good men I knew and admired.

As I walked into the sanctuary, Pastor Pitts began the gospel with a scripture from Ephesians 4:23–32, saying:

> And be renewed in the spirit of your mind; And that ye put on the new man, which after God is created in righteousness and true holiness. Wherefore putting away lying, speak every man truth with his neighbour: for we are members one of another. Be ye angry, and sin not: let not the sun go down upon your wrath: Neither give place to the devil. Let him that stole steal no more: but rather let him labour, working with his hands the thing which is good, that he may have to give to him that needeth. Let no

corrupt communication proceed out of your mouth, but that which is good to the use of edifying that it may minister grace unto the hearers. And grieve not the holy Spirit of God, whereby ye are sealed unto the day of redemption. Let all bitterness, and wrath, and anger, and clamour, and evil speaking, be put away from you, with all malice: And be ye kind one to another, tenderhearted, forgiving one another, even as God for Christ's sake hath forgiven you.

I sat and reflected on what I overheard: "And be renewed in the spirit of your mind: And that ye put on the new man, which after God is created in righteousness and true holiness." Blessed are the eyes to see the things that ye see and so are the ears to hear. I took that as if it were directed to me. To give light to those who sit in darkness and, in the shadow of death, guide our feet into the way of peace. Things began to be clearer as I patiently waited for Pastor Pitts to finish the service.

"Brother, I am honored to have you in my presence. That scar on your face is a depiction of the pain in your eyes, I take it?" Pastor Pitts asked. Those were the first words he said as he sat next to me. It had been months since I had been around Pastor Pitts. The last time he saw me, the scar across my face was not there.

My reply to him was reserved. I could not speak. I was helpless, defenseless. Weak. I had done things to try and fill a void, in search of something in my life that had been absent. I had walked through so much shit in my life. To try to explain myself was hard. Most of the time I was misunderstood, but he understood. He understood the pain and agony

I felt, the crosses I've been nailed to, the wrath of my actions I had committed over the years for my survival. I was just an empty, broken man in his company who was seeking love and direction. Pastor Pitts spoke directly to me.

"I get it, Alexander, but you need to know this: you are a good man, Alexander. You lived a life based on what you knew, what you were taught growing up, and the things you've witnessed. We do not choose the family we are born into, and sometimes things happen that we did not choose, but we *can* choose how we respond. The things we go through, that pain is just life happening. It is lessons, son. We are humans. I nor anyone else could condemn you for that. I do not judge a man based on his personality but his heart. You have a good heart, Alexander. That I sense and that I know. Do not let the world measure who you are. They do not have your experiences. There was a time in my life when I would have cast judgment on you, but you taught me a lesson. You changed how I view people like you. I would have looked down on you because of your lack of education. But you taught me to think differently, and I am thankful for that.

"You are much smarter and wiser than you give yourself credit for. Just because you do not know something does not cancel out the things you *do* know. You taught me that. So do not rob yourself of the blessings from the tools you do have. Because they are what got you here. From your father's ashes came glory; everything you have and will build came from the ashes your father left behind. We cannot change the past, but we can decide on how we move forward. What is it you want to do moving forward?"

I replied in a shaky voice, "I want to be a worthy servant to God." Tears settled in as I formed my last word. I leaned over and cried in the pastor's arms.

He held me tightly and said, "It's all right, son. God's got you!"

Hell cannot make a prison that God cannot break into. It started with silent prayers I had within, just being thankful for accepting a man like me. Men like us. Receiving me in His arms.

I know I do not deserve it, but I am here, Father. The choices I made in life were only to fill an empty void. The paths I chose before were trying to fill shoes that were not mine. Following the path of men before me. But if it weren't for that path I walked on, I wouldn't be in the place I am in now. I love this place. You took me in when no one else would, you made sure the angels above protected me from all harm that could or would come my way. Thank you.

This was the first time in my life I acknowledged the man I was, understanding the wrongs I had done. Having the confidence and strength to accept my wrongdoings and the self-desire to change my ways. To the renewing of the mind, opening the eyes of my heart, not just to love myself but others. It took years for me to get here, a lot of great suffering, destruction, disappointment, but by His Grace, I was here. I felt free.

For the first time in my life, I heard a voice in my head that said "I love you" as I was speaking to myself. Tears formed as they rolled down my cheeks into the palm of my hands. I've witnessed grown men and women cry during service from hearing the gospel or the praise team praising—those were tears of joy. Author Jonathan Harnisch said, "The strongest people are not those who show strength in front of the world but those who fight and win battles that others do not know anything about." It allowed me to be present, understanding where I came from to get me to where I am. Men and women cry because they have overcome something that weighed heavy on their lives in their hearts. Many people don't see the ashes, they don't see the crosses we have been nailed to, they don't see every tear we have shed, they don't see it—but those are the brothers and sisters you see standing on their feet, arms stretched above their heads, feet stomping on the grounds they stand on, shouting as loud as the room allows them to, dancing on the devil's head. Those are the brothers and sisters I want to stand in partnership with.

I attended church religiously. Every Sunday for service and Bible study on Wednesdays. Thursday was group day, where I would join the Impact Ministry group to worship outside the church to further my studies, growth, and faith. I was baptized and became an active member of that church. I pursued positive and healthy ways to keep myself occupied so I would not allow myself to drift off. I knew what it was like when you fell to the wayside. I knew what it felt like when you committed a sin against yourself. Where depression and self-hatred would overpower your world. I had to defend myself against myself by getting involved in healthy actions. The why and where God was planting me, the soil was richer and produced greater fruit.

I sought out work because that was part of the change, the growth. The majority of workplaces I have worked at were mostly all warehouses, and I quit most of those because I was bored or they fired me. I was never meant to be an employee; I was the employer, but we have to start somewhere. I needed something that required being more hands-on. Something physical. I was still lacking certain skill sets, but I had the ability to learn and, with the right mentor, that was valuable.

Working at a furniture warehouse at night, my shift was just about to end. Coming in my direction were two African American men. Much older, somewhere in their forties and fifties. I introduced myself respectfully to both gentlemen as they then made known to me who they were. Mike and Phil. Phil was a hustler from Detroit. His hands were rough and swollen but his shake was firm. Phil reminded me of a character named LeRoi "King" Tremain from a book I once read, *Standing at the Scratch Line* by Guy Johnson. Phil was the foreman of the two. Mike was his helper. This was a crew of men that delivered furniture to homes. Phil was also the driver. I asked Phil if he was looking for additional help. I knew nothing about moving furniture or dealing with customers. He took me under his wing. That moment changed my life. Him agreeing to hire me opened me up to a skill set I did not have and led me to understand that I could be hired anywhere around the world by having moving/delivery experience. But the real tool I obtained by being under Phil was my work ethic. Joseph Conrad wrote in his novella *Heart of Darkness*, "I don't like work—no man does—but I like what is in the work—the chance to find yourself." Phil created a monster. He fine-tuned what was hidden. Taking personal inventory of myself allowed me to make new discoveries. I was a savage and I refused to allow any man or woman to outwork me. Phil taught me that.

Phil showed me how to break down a piano and strip it for its brass, set up a junk removal service where we would go out and knock down a shed from a customer's home and throw the broken pieces away at a waste-management landfill. During move jobs, he didn't allow me to use hand trucks or four-wheelers. We carried everything by hand and straps. We would put a washing machine or refrigerator on a pad to wiggle it out of the door without carrying it. Before he taught me the tricks of the trade, he taught me the game. I never once outshined Phil; I was his student. The proper lesson of a foremen is to make sure that whoever is on the other end of that piece can handle it. Your life is in their hands and their life is in your hands. That is why Phil and I carried every piece. Mike was happy I came on board because it allowed him to sleep in the truck and read the daily word while Phil and I got busy. Phil taught me how to finesse customers out of tips. Tips are everything. If you have a daily habit, the tips come in handy; if you're broke and have no money to eat, the tips will feed you. We almost fought once, inside a customer's home, because of my lack of understanding. It resulted in tearing the love seat in front of a customer. This wasn't the first time we had torn pieces of furniture or put large dinner plate–sized holes in a wall. This came from lack of ignorance, not paying attention to his body language. But I wasn't going to fight Phil in the back of the trailer with the doors closed. I loved Phil. Whatever he asked, I would do. So he found a way to get back at me. It was raining outside as we finished up the customer's move. We were in an open lot, not many cars in the parking lot, but he could not see outside his mirrors. So, instead he asked to me get out and guide him, which I did. I got back in the truck soaking wet, but I still got paid at the end of the day. I have a lot of respect for Phil as a man and the type of work ethic he had. I had never met a man like him. I am thankful that I did. Because a part of him is a part of me. The oil that ran from his vessel carried into me. That is why I work as hard as I do.

I fell in love with the hustle, the challenge, the grind. Not just because of the aggressiveness or competitiveness, but because we pushed each other to become better. I knew when it came to moving furniture I was a beast, but my best work came from when I moved on and started working at Elite Relocation. Those boys had never met a man like me. A dog like me. They were about using hand trucks and four-wheelers, working smart. I was not trained like that. I'd pick a sofa up and carry it on my shoulders. I told Andi, a coworker of mine at this company, to pick up a hutch with me so we could carry it together. He said no, it was too heavy. I told him he didn't even try. A coworker I considered a brother looked this man, Andi, in the eye and called him a pussy to his face. That day, I knew I wanted to be on every job with Carllis. But for Andi, I told him to go inside and fill the customer's fish tank for her. He made multiple trips from the bathroom to the living room filling her fish tank.

Moving is a man's sport, a woman's too. I have carried

dressers and sofas with women. I apply the same pressure on them as I would on a man. When it comes to work, I couldn't care less about your outside life. You don't earn my respect from what you do outside of work. What we do in the field is how you gain my respect. And if you fall short of what I expect, we will have to address it. Because moving will either break you down to where you don't want to come back, or it will push you to limits you never thought of surpassing. I either made weaker men out of men because they were weak and gave up, or I made better men out of men.

Carllis, David, José, and Danny—these men saw firsthand how hungry I was. I would lace six fifty-three-foot trailers back to back from small to oversized tires by hand myself. My hunger, my drive, pushed Carllis and David to be better than they were before I met them. Carllis and David would try their best to keep up with my efforts. David would risk the bones in his body to outdo me, but as I had told them and Danny before, I would not let anyone outwork me. Danny was the employer of Elite Relocation; that man gave me an opportunity to work and represent his organization, and I did so proudly. José pushed me to become a better mover. He challenged me on every job. Tested my strength when it came to picking up a piece of furniture, loading the truck with machinery that valued over a million dollars. He not only wanted me to do well, but he encouraged me to follow my plan, asking me, "What are you waiting for?" This conversation with him is the reason I moved on from Elite Relocation.

The strides I was making in my life were providing peace.

Creating new space for new energy. I kept evolving the idea of the man I wanted to become. Create the space for the life I chose to create with the tools I had obtained over the span of my lifetime. I kept making one choice at a time.

The next decision I made was to join the film committee at my church. I knew nothing about film or production, but I wanted to learn, to take on new challenges. I was offered a position to work the angles of the camera during services. Whenever the pastor would move, I would make sure his new frame was ready to be displayed on the monitor. It was not fulfilling and it took me away from being present during service, but I did not give up on the idea of learning filmmaking. I wanted to pursue that route, be involved with storytelling. Using my life, my story for creativeness. I have met men and women along my path where I could use their journey to feed into my imagination. Film became my next goal. I never wanted to be an actor, but I wanted to learn how to tap into the layers of a character. Using real emotions to add life into your character. Understanding the bookshelf method, I was able to go into my past life and search for moments I could apply to the character to provide that surreal feeling. Everything I did came from my life. A moment where if I wanted to bring out a positive, feel-good emotion, I would think about the time my uncle and I used to wrestle and box with each other. We had a theme song called "Bodies" by Drowning Pool or "The Beautiful People" by Marilyn Manson. Those songs meant it was war. He or I was on the attack. I would come around the corner and pop him in the head with a pillow thinking it was a chair, or he'd turn off the room lights and rush me. Everything wasn't always violent. So, I would resort to that book on my bookshelf.

Once I got the basics of acting, I directed my focus to production. I enrolled in a local college that offered classes. I would use the school equipment to shoot my productions. I learned lighting, editing, sound, and camerawork. I learned everything that came with production. I learned what I needed to learn to make what I wanted to happen.

I wrote a feature film script called *Twenty-Two*. The character, Jacob, was created around the philosophies I believed about how a man should conduct himself. "Greater love hath no man than this, that a man lay down his life for his friends" (John 15:13). The script was built around murder to survive or be consumed by the ones who are out to get you, but instead of glorifying the acts of violence, I wanted to give the idea that a man should not be afraid to kill. Not that you want to, but that you will. We all have a killer bone inside of us; some are just closer to the surface than others. But when it comes to protecting the lives of the ones you love, there is no limit to how far a man is willing to go. Sacrifice your life to protect the lives of the ones you love. One of the qualities of a great man is a protector. Writing, acting, production, it was all a beautiful hobby for me. I was able to express myself through the arts. As a child, I would write just to get through reality. I never thought I would eventually write to put something on its feet. To give something to the world to see. To watch. To read. But my travels in life allowed me to make it happen, not just that, but to the woman I met!

CHAPTER EIGHT

Let Love Lead You Home

I now believe heaven lies at the foot of a woman, similar to what Prophet Muhammad said. When we love, we strive to become better than we are. I made changes in my life to become better than the man I was. But when I met her, I wanted to become better than the man I currently was. I understand if I were to have met her before I did, I would not have had the tools nor be equipped to be with a woman such as herself. Immature in many ways. Emotionally unstable. As men, we are supposed to go into a relationship with a plan, a vision. A goal. The partner we choose to go into that relationship with, she is there to help us see our vision, our goals, our plans through. A woman makes her man better. It's in their nature. That's why they are mothers. They produce life. I believe any relationship one has, there must be growth. One of the tools I used a lot was self-reflection. The art of self-reflection was a tool I learned by reading the book, *Think and Grow Rich: A Black Choice* by Dennis Kimbro and Napoleon Hill. I reflected on everything I did. I would go back to the lessons I had with people. I always watched and saw how men were better and happier when they were with the person they honestly were in love with. I wanted that. That was the void in my life. Until I met Latonzia. I met her outside of her apartment complex.

She started driving in my direction, so I walked in front of her car. I knew she would have stopped and the guy she dropped off, well, they were together, but obviously he did not care much about her to make sure she left the parking lot safely. So I approached her and we engaged in conversation. She said, "You don't want me," and I replied, "You don't know what I want!" If you were to ask me if she was the woman I wanted, my response would have been, "Does a bear shit in the woods and wipe his ass with a rabbit?" Without her even knowing, she was exactly what I wanted.

She had her own issues she was sorting out, and the man she was with was more attentive to the television than he was to her. It was only a matter of time before she left him, and when she did, that is how our story began. She waited some time before she called. But, when she eventually did some months later, I was in a dark place.

My mind started to play back moments I had shared with my uncle. There was a moment where I was disobedient to his words and disrespectful with my actions. Flashbacks of that moment weighed heavily on me. I was never fully able to explain what had happened to my uncle.

The rage, his emotions, would not allow him to hear me out. I had taken something from him without his permission. He owned a freshly designed, custom jacket. I wore this jacket out one night, and in doing so, I ran into some trouble.

A member from the Legion of Doom, Rio, invited me to go out with him and his girlfriend to a local bar one night. Inside the bar, I walked away from the two so I could use the bathroom. The line to the bathroom was long, and I was not about to wait. I walked right in, went straight to an open stall, and as soon as I did, six men circled me. Understanding the situation, I walked out and told Rio what just happened. We went outside and waited. Rio told his girlfriend to go wait in the car and have it running.

We waited until one of the men came out, and as he did, he came out with his girlfriend. Rio said "Hold on, let him walk into the dark," and once he walked out from under the lights, Rio said, "Go!" Before the man could turn his back to see me coming, I was already there. I shoved his girlfriend out of the way and pressed his body against the wall. Every punch I threw was with the intentions of breaking this man's face. His girlfriend got up and started screaming. Rio came from behind and did what he had to do to shut her up. Her screaming brought attention, as we knew it would. I looked over and saw her body drop, and then the police were coming after us.

As we ran, I tossed the jacket. It was heavy, and they knew what I was wearing. I was able to get away, but in the midst of running, I saw an elderly couple at a stop sign. I quickly opened the back door and jumped in their car and had them drop me off where I wanted.

The night when I had these flashbacks, I cried. Because my uncle was hurt by my actions and I never got the chance to apologize. My world started to seem dark again. I once heard someone say the darkest hour of the night is right before the sunrise. That following morning is when she called. We sat on the phone for hours just talking. Telling corny jokes. "What does a fish say when he hits the wall?"

or "What does gold say to silver when they meet at the bar?" When she waited on my response, I didn't have answers to her jokes. I did not know how to respond. Instantly, thoughts surfaced, telling me, *You're stupid, this woman now knows your level of intellect.* So, I quickly became aggressive with her over the phone. She hung up on me. I was not going to call her back, but she called me back and told me never let a woman/girlfriend/wife hang up on you or go to bed upset with you. All of this was new to me. I had never felt what it was like to be drawn to a woman. I never experienced a relationship with a woman before, due to the life I lived. But this was cool. I enjoyed the presence we had, even over the phone. We sat and watched TV together then; on commercial breaks, we would discuss what just happened. Exchanged thoughts. I never had cared to be talkative. I did not like people. But when the energy in the room was good, everything just fit into place.

Her parents owned a logistics company. She would tell me that logistics is a field that will never stop. Something will always need to be imported and exported. She would talk about how her family—her father—would go out on runs with helpers. Helping him do his deliveries through-out the day. This was how I learned about the idea of being a mover. From the conversations she and I had. As time went on, we started venturing toward the idea of trucking. I knew nothing about trucking, as I didn't know much about moving. All I knew was if I inserted myself into what I was pursuing, I would make it happen. Trucking became the forefront of my pursuits. I wanted to create a trucking company that she and I could shape over time.

Obtain contracts by having direct shippers, purchase trucks, hire employees, etc. I knew I could have her do the day-to-day operations in the office while I was out in the field. That is how you build together. There was the plan, the vision, the goal. Lady of Choice Transit, LLC, became the trucking company I pursued.

Growing up, I did not have family that was in trucking, so I had to learn. I went to school to get my commercial driver's license—that was easy. Failed my first time trying to do a blindside parallel park with a tractor and trailer. But I passed the second time. I was hired on to a major carrier as company driver for fifteen months, then started my own. Life on the road had its moments, but because of the road I traveled to get me to that moment, I was prepared for it. Pissing in an empty bottle you just finished drinking out of, putting a garbage bag in a bucket just so you could squat to take a shit inside the truck. Eating one meal a day and drinking just enough fluids so you don't have to stop to use the bathroom often. Negative five degrees in Colorado, but you can't use the bunk heater because of a lack of fuel and no fuel stop within the next ninety miles, so you sleep in the cold just so you can save gas. Sleeping in random rest areas, truck stops, having to wait in line to shower after another man just got out, never really knowing who was sleeping next to you. Staying in locations where the safest thing for you to do is strap your seat belt through the door so no one can try to break in while you sleep. No truckers move around without having protection. Some have pistols, some have knives; they have what they have to defend themselves.

I made life on the road work for me. I loved trucking. It was fun. Being able to travel different places, see different things, starting your day at three a.m. and watching the sun rise as you are on I-5 going through California up to Washington. Life was beautiful. Having interactions with men and women you didn't know before. Brother JohnnyJon taught me the game. Taught me how to structure a truck company. Build it from the ground up. Buy you a few trucks, hire you a few solid employees, obtain your own authority, have your own trailers—but if you really want to capitalize on the market, have your own in-house broker. Now you are in the game. The more you grow, the larger the slice of the pie.

JohnnyJon taught me the game, but Sir G. Henry taught me the rules of the road. I was trained by him. Driving ten hours a day, showering not so often, how to utilize my hours within a day just so I wouldn't have to do a reset, because when you do a reset you are not working and that means you are not making money. He wanted to make sure I could handle what was to come. Throwing iron on tires because the chain law is in effect. Everything I knew about being a driver came from Sir G. Henry and everything else I learned was developed by being out on the road. Truck school only teaches you how to pass the DMV test, so everything else you must learn in the real world. It's not their job to make sure you are fully capable to do the job. They leave that up to the company that hires you on.

Krazy Carl was a friend, but I loved him as a brother. When I had mechanical problems, he would provide solutions. He'd figure out what truck codes meant, provide knowledge, such as do not stay coupled to a trailer when the mechanical tech is welding on the trailer. If you do, disconnect your airlines. If not, the electrical waves will run through the kingpin and it will kill your battery. Conversing about random topics—about life, trucking. He talked to me about survival tactics. The sulfur from a black match you chew or swallow goes into your bloodstream, so as you sweat the ticks and mosquitoes stay off you. Different matches have a different taste.

The month I met Krazy Carl, I had begun to run low on fuel. The nearest fuel station I knew of was ninety miles out. I did not have the luxury of opening a map or using a phone to find something that was near. Krazy Carl, for about an hour, was on the search to find where I could get fuel from. He sent me multiple locations that were on my route. He did everything he could within his cable tow to be at my aid. I loved this brother for all he had done for me. As I stated before, a quote by William Butler Yeats reads, "There are no strangers here; only friends you haven't met yet."

I set up a small gym up inside my truck. A weight bench, plates, bars, kettlebell. I stayed active. Working out either in the morning, between shifts, or at night is what helped me get through each day. It was how I made trucking work for me. I cooked meals in my truck. Eating steak, fish, salmon, with white rice and potatoes. Oatmeal and eggs for breakfast. I created a world for myself and I loved every bit of it.

During my downtime, I was working out. A brother named Paul Mac walked up to me and asked me, "You keep all that workout equipment in your truck?" That was how the conversation began. This was the same brother who gave me the resources I needed to go out and purchase my first truck. He laid out his blueprint of what he did and I just followed the steps. That conversation we had was one of the greatest conversations I have ever had with a person. One of the greatest experiences I had on the road was meeting this brother Paul Mac, besides the other time a less fortunate brother who was homeless walked up to me at the fuel island and asked me to lead the prayer. Those are two experiences I will never forget. But the conversation with Paul Mac, it was different. This conversation had substance, spiritual matter. Angelic activity circled around us. As my fist pulled back from his fist from the dap I gave him before parting, a black-and-orange butterfly flew out.

The butterfly symbolizes great transformation and growth. Orange and black, the rebirth of me. My mother gave birth to my earthly body, but she did not give birth to what I represented. My heavenly father gave birth to my mind, wisdom, and spirit. All my travels in life, the lessons I have learned, the people I have met, they all have played a significant part in my life. Being locked up, it helped me see what my purpose in life was. All the creative effort and work I had done was not my purpose. Starting my own truck school was not my purpose. It was part of that, but it was not the whole. Leaving a foundation behind that is directed to aid men and women who are or were incarcerated, extending an opportunity to come on board with the foundation where we can help position them in a job where they can better themselves, help build and create tools they can use in their everyday lives, providing an opportunity to be trained and employed as truck drivers or mechanics, helping them create opportunities not just for themselves but for others around them. That is the purpose. That is how you leave your mark on this earth. Being a worthy servant.

We never count how many choices we make in a day. I knew the choices I made in my life would come back around. The officer told me, "Life is a full circle. Eventually your actions will catch up to you. You just do not know when, where, how, or why!" Here is how.

While out on the road, I received a phone call from my ol' lady. I picked up and answered, but it was a man on the other end. These were his words: "I know you are out on the road. You need to get home, and when you do, call me, or I will kill your girl."

I hung up the phone and just went into thought. I had to get out of the truck. The anger and confusion would make it unsafe for me to drive. Never once are you supposed to drive upset. My mind was so gone, nothing made sense. So any action I was to take would not have been from logic. Leaving my truck in Arizona, I drove a rental car back to Chicago. It took less time than it would have with a tractor trailer. Back home, I made that phone call, letting them know I was home. I did not have time to try and figure things out. I was too far behind. He was smart. He played by the rules of the world. Make people come to you using bait. He had control, so that gave him the power.

In that phone call, I received the answers to the questions

in my head. It was the older son of the judge from years ago. He lived in Tijuana, Mexico. I respected this man's actions and how far he was willing to go with things. He told me, "Get your affairs in order and come the following day. We will make an exchange." A life for a life. It was a blood debt that was owed. Mine for hers. It all made sense, what my uncle said about having attachments. Do not commit to anyone. This guy had me where he wanted me. Any action outside of what he advised would put her at risk. I could not afford to take that risk. I could live with the consequences to my actions when it pertained to me and I was the only one I had to think about, but being in a relationship, I no longer could think for just myself. I put her before me. So, I knew what needed to be done.

That same morning, when we ended the phone call, I met with two people followed by visiting my uncle. The first person was Lil Stace. He was having breakfast when I walked into his home. It was him, his wife, and their newborn. They were all caught off guard. He did not expect me to be there. Sometimes, the person we would take a bullet for is also the one who could be holding the gun. Lil Stace was behind this act. But I respected him; I'd killed and would have taken a bullet for this man, but I understood why he did what he did. I had not held up to my obligation of the order. But he needed to hear what I had to say. I told his wife to go stand "nose and toes" against the kitchen wall and give the baby to Lil Stace. As she did so, I pulled up a chair and sat down with Lil Stace as he held his child. I told him I knew he gave me up. He tried to speak, but I did not allow it. I told him to just listen.

I told him if I wanted to, I could have killed him and his family in the kitchen and thought nothing of it. I told him I could put the pistol in his daughter's mouth and make him watch me slaughter his entire family. But thankfully, I was no longer the man I used to be.

I asked him, "Do you know what real forgiveness is?" I did not want him to talk, so I told him to nod his head yes or no. I told him forgiveness was when you have the ability to do something to that person, but you choose not to. I forgave Lil Stace, but I made it clear that he knew of my position, because his entire life could have changed in one breath.

I stood up from the table, and as I walked toward the door, Lil Stace spoke. "Take care of yourself, man."

I replied, "God's got me," and closed the door to his home.

Pastor Pitts was the second person I went to visit. I believed in his leadership and trusted in his vision. I believe one of the greatest gifts God gave man is the gift of vision. The things we become passionate about, the sacrifices we make for every mission we are on, comes from the function of one's heart. My vision in life would let it be known I was here. So, I conveyed my plans to him and gave him the resources to see those plans through.

He asked, "Where are you going, Lex?"

Softly spoken, I replied, "I do not know," with a half-smile.

He knew what I meant. We hugged and I told him I had to leave. Before I could walk out, Pastor Pitts touched my thigh and called me Israel. He said, "Your name is no longer Alexander Lee Jr. You are now named Israel. For you have striven with God and with men, and prevailed."

As he said that, I became emotional. My eyes became watery; I understood each word he spoke. The battles I had faced. Each challenge I withstood on the path of my travels tried me in all aspects of life: spiritual, emotional, physical, and sexual. Everything was a test or celebration in life, and this was the celebration.

Lastly, I went to visit my uncle's grave. I wanted him to hear me. Let him know I am the man I am because of him and by God's grace, I have made it this far. I made it on my own. I looked back from where I started to where I am now. I was proud of the man I had grown to become, and I knew he would be proud, too, without having to hear him say it. That night, while sitting with him, I felt a warm sensation. A feeling you get from the presence of someone being with you. My journey, my travels, I had never traveled alone, and when I thought I was alone, that was the weaker me trying to get the best of me. God reassured me that I was not unaided. He never said life would be easy, but He also never said I would go through it alone. The shortest scripture in the Bible is that Jesus wept.

The following day, as I woke up, I could hear the birds chirping, the sounds of a trumpet playing in the distance. Heaven's light shined down upon me as it sat at the top of the clouds that formed Jacob's ladder. The same homeless lady who had given me a blanket so many months before was there across from me when I woke. She smiled and said, "It's time." I understood what she meant. I rose to my feet as she moved in my direction with a necklace in her hand. As she put the necklace around my neck, I looked down and saw it was a small charm of a Bible that opened to pages of the Lord's Prayer. The lady looked me in the eyes and said, "Job well done, my boy!"

Once at the exchange, Latonzia and I looked at each other and I told her how beautiful she was as I kissed her on the forehead and said, "Everything I have done since I met you was to become better than the man I was when I met you! I hope that when you look in the mirror and see that glow shining on your forehead, that is because you have gold in your soul, and I pray all your dreams come true and you build that house down in Atlanta so as you bathe in your tub, you'll be able to overlook that vegetable garden you spoke of."

I understood what my uncle meant when he said, "Let love lead you home," because now I was at peace. A warrior's greatest reward is his peace. As I made my steps, I heard a voice, and it was not an echo. The spirit overflowed inside of me. It filled me to my core. The voice I heard said, "Job well done, my boy!"

HE IS I and I AM HIM
THE END!

THIS IS NOT THE END OF ALEXANDER LEE JR.'S
STORY

Lady of Choice Productions
DREAM to INSPIRE

ACKNOWLEDGMENTS

God, my Angels, and myself (Darren S. Hardaway Jr.)

ABOUT THE AUTHOR

Darren S. Hardaway Jr. is a man of many convictions, traveled many paths, but he never allowed his past to dictate his future. He is now the owner of Lady of Choice Transit, LLC, a trucking company. He has written and produced multiple short films under Lady of Choice Productions and has created a widely known T-shirt printing company, Hardaway Custom Hats & Apparel. The adversities he has braved throughout his life have given him the wits to create and publish *Black Butterfly: Rebirth of a Beautiful Soul*, a testimony of an extraordinary man, a man who is proud to be the man he is. Darren S. Hardaway Jr. has made his own way!

Lady of Choice Transit, LLC, "Make Your Own Way"

CPSIA information can be obtained
at www.ICGtesting.com
Printed in the USA
LVHW090339090521
686901LV00008B/458